CW00816008

Guide to Freshwater Invertebrates

Michael Dobson
Simon Pawley
Melanie Fletcher
Anne Powell
Freshwater Biological Association

Freshwater Biological Association
Scientific Publication No. 68
2012

Editor: Alan Crowden
Production and Publications Manager: Karen Rouen

Published by the Freshwater Biological Association,
The Ferry Landing, Far Sawrey, Ambleside, Cumbria LA22 0LP, UK

(Registered Charity No.214440)

First printed 2012
Reprinted 2013

ISBN 978-0-900386-80-0

ISSN 0367-1887

A tribute to T.T. Macan from the
Freshwater Biological Association

Contents

Foreword

I am grateful to the Council of the Freshwater Biological Association for their invitation to write a foreword to this successor volume to *A Guide to Freshwater Invertebrate Animals* by my father, T.T. (Kit) Macan - first published by Longman in 1959.

The Guide was only one of a number of books which he wrote during his research career. It was not the longest, or the most demanding. But I think it was his favourite because it served to open the world of fresh water to those who wanted to learn about it. He was sometimes surprised to discover how far its reach extended: the Spanish text, published (with permission) in 1975 by the University of Navarra as *Invertebrados de agua dulce* remains a cherished trophy.

His approach to freshwater ecology was entirely low-tech. Equipped with his rucksack containing a pond-net, a couple of sorting dishes, a lens, a notebook plus a packed lunch and accompanied by his Labrador dog, he had all he needed for a day's field work. The only laboratory back-up he required was a decent optical microscope. The day's work was doubly satisfactory if, as a consequence, someone was inspired to take up the quest.

He never held a full-time teaching appointment, though he much enjoyed short stints at the Universities of Idaho, Ohio and Toulouse. But his support for temporary summer assistants, young researchers working at Ferry House and the annual Easter Class helped launch many worthwhile scientific careers. The purpose of *A Guide to Freshwater Invertebrate Animals* was to equip those embarking on the study of freshwater ecology with a handy manual to fit in the pocket (or at least in the rucksack).

In the fifty years that have passed since its publication, the pressures on our freshwater resources have grown hugely. So has the need to understand what lives in them. Kit Macan would be delighted that one of the basic tools to guide people towards that understanding had appeared in new and updated form.

Tom Macan
Cumbria

The legacy of Macan and the need for this book

There can be few enthusiasts of freshwater biology in Britain who have not come across the works of T.T. Macan. The author of the first scientific publication of the Freshwater Biological Association (FBA) in 1939, on Corixidae, Macan also wrote guides to the remaining water bugs (1941), gastropod snails (1960), malacostracan crustaceans (1960), larval mayflies (1961) and adult caddisflies (1973), for several of which he also wrote revised editions. In 1951 he co-authored a volume in the New Naturalist series: *Life in Lakes and Rivers*. It is, however, for *A Guide to Freshwater Invertebrate Animals* (1959) that he is best known. This little book, in its distinctive blue dust jacket, was written out of his strong desire to educate and help those interested in fresh waters. Although long out of print, the book is still widely sought as a simple yet effective guide to the invertebrate fauna of lakes and rivers. Arranged as little more than a single extended key, its ease of use has inspired budding freshwater ecologists for over 50 years.

Thomas Townley Macan was born in 1910. His own interest in freshwater biology was inspired while studying at Cambridge, where he became close friends with Hugh Cary Gilson, later Director of the FBA, but his first professional work was in marine biology, studying starfish in the Indian Ocean. In 1935 he became one of the two resident naturalists at the recently founded FBA, and there he remained – barring wartime service in the army – until his retirement in 1976.

Macan's enthusiasm for encouraging others – whether his research assistants, students attending the famous 'Easter Classes' held at the FBA's Windermere headquarters from the 1930s to the 1970s, or the wider public – never waned. His little blue book was revised twice and he was working on a fourth edition when he died in 1984.

This guide is intended as a tribute to Macan and his legacy. By producing it at this time, the FBA hopes it can go some way towards repeating the success of Macan, by creating a guide that is simple to use and inspires a new generation of freshwater biologists. Like Macan, we believe that the best way to structure such a book is in the form of keys that guide the reader to a successful identification. Also like Macan, we are aware that sometimes rigidly sticking to a dichotomous key is less helpful than alternative approaches, and where appropriate we have made use of different methods to aid identification.

We see this as a work in progress. Many readers will disagree with our approach and may find that our keys have flaws. As with any FBA publication, we would welcome any comments and constructive criticisms. For those who need more advice or further information, about recording schemes, specialist societies and training courses, along with updates on identification, corrections, new species or significant new distributions, or other specialist information, we refer you to our website: www.fba.org.uk. The opportunity afforded by the internet to modify, update and upgrade in real time is something that we are sure T.T. Macan would have appreciated.

The authors
Cumbria

Introduction

The scope of this book

The aim of this book is to assist you in identifying invertebrate animals that you may come across in freshwater environments. It is not comprehensive: there are simply far too many species and most groups require specialist knowledge or skills, and often specialist equipment. The book provides a guide to the more commonly encountered groups and points to further information, where it is available, for those who want to pursue identification to a higher level.

Invertebrates are animals that lack a backbone, a simple definition that covers a huge variety of forms. This book concentrates upon the larger, more conspicuous groups of invertebrates that live in fresh waters (macroinvertebrates), but also covers the smaller ones. The Protozoa, normally microscopic single-celled organisms, were formerly classed within the Animal Kingdom, and were included by Macan in his guide to invertebrates. They are, however, now more normally considered to be part of the Protist Kingdom, along with single-celled and multicellular algae. They are therefore not included in this book, as their diversity of forms, small size and clear overlap in features with some algae make them candidates for separate consideration.

True plants and fungi are not covered by this book, being mentioned only where they are important for understanding invertebrates. Similarly the vertebrates, a relatively species-poor but extremely important group covering fish, amphibians, reptiles, birds and mammals, are outside the scope of this book. The boundary between invertebrates and vertebrates is artificial, but widely established, hence our use of it here.

Invertebrates generally pass through several clearly separate life stages, often with an immature larval stage that is morphologically very different to the adult stage (see fig. 1). For some groups, we have not attempted to provide keys for the larval stages (such as the free swimming or even parasitic larvae of mussels); for others, the larvae are the life stages you are most likely to come across. Most freshwater invertebrates are aquatic throughout their lives but, among the larger and more conspicuous animals, most insect groups are aquatic only in the larval stage, the flying adults being terrestrial (with a few beetles being aquatic only in the adult stage). This book covers only the aquatic stages of these animals. If the animal you are trying to identify is a larva, then the key will work best with late stage larvae, and very young larvae may not be possible to identify with any precision.

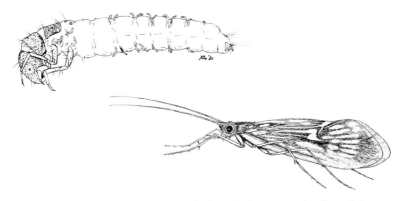

Fig. 1. Caddisflies: above, an example of a larva; below, example of an adult.

Classification of animals: understanding the names

In order to use this guide effectively, it helps to have an understanding of the different levels used in the classification of organisms. For those who are not fully familiar with the system used, we provide a short introduction below.

All animals have their place in the taxonomic hierarchy, a system of classifying species according to the degree to which they are related to each other. The classification adopted has several clear divisions.

At the top is the kingdom. Once there were only two recognised kingdoms: plants and animals. Now we appreciate that life is more complex than that, especially at the microscopic level. The concept of five kingdoms – animals, plants, fungi, protists (algae and single-celled organisms) and bacteria – has been widely accepted since the 1970s, and current thinking is that the bacteria should be further subdivided into several kingdoms. This guide, however, only covers organisms that are in the Animal Kingdom.

Each kingdom is divided into phyla (singular: phylum), each of which is divided into classes. Some phyla may have only one or two classes, whereas others have half a dozen or more. Each class is divided into orders, which are divided into families.

Below the family are genera (singular: genus), into which species are placed. If you look at the scientific name of an animal, it will be presented as two words, the so-called binomial system of naming. The first word, which should always begin with a capital letter, is the generic name; the second, which should never have a capital letter, even if it is given in honour of a named person or place, is the specific name. The whole should be written in italics, or underlined.

So, if we take the stonefly *Brachyptera putata*, we know it is in the genus *Brachyptera* and the species name is *putata*. It shares its genus with a closely related species, *Brachyptera risi* (which can be abbreviated to *B. risi* where there is no doubt what the *B.* stands for). These two species, in turn, are in the family Taeniopterygidae, the order Plecoptera, the class Insecta (which includes most of the insects), the phylum Arthropoda and the kingdom Animalia. Its hierarchical classification is:

Kingdom: Animalia
Phylum: Arthropoda
Class: Insecta
Order: Plecoptera
Family: Taeniopterygidae
Species: *Brachyptera putata*

All animals have these six levels of classification. In some cases, where differences are not enough to justify a full division, there will be subclasses, superorders, subfamilies, and so on. Higher levels of classification have no specific rules for the names given, but family names always end in 'idae'; similarly subfamilies, into which a family may be divided, have names ending in 'inae' and tribes, a potential further subdivision, have names ending in 'ini'. Going in the other direction, several families may be classified together into a superfamily, below the level of order, whose name end in 'oidea'.

The naming of animals does not simply provide a system to help with identification, but also recognises the degree to which they are related to each other. Unfortunately for the naturalist this means that as opinions change, so occasionally will names. Many species have been shifted from one genus to another, so that the name you see in one guide is not necessarily the same as the name in another produced at a later date. For example, Macan refers to the native crayfish as *Astacus pallipes*, but modern thinking has removed it from the genus *Astacus* and placed it in *Austropotamobius*, so its currently accepted name is *Austropotamobius pallipes*. Furthermore, what was once considered to be a good species is occasionally found to be the same as another that was given a different name and, by the law of priority, the earliest given name takes preference. A good example is the snail known for many years as *Potamopyrgus jenkinsi*; this is now considered to be the same as a species known as *P. antipodarium*, whose name takes priority, so *P. jenkinsi* is no longer valid. Occasionally both names are required to change; the freshwater world has a good example, a very common gastropod snail known for many years as *Lymnaea peregra*, whose currently accepted name is *Radix balthica*! Freshwater organisms include many whose names have changed in these ways; we have tried to point out those where examination of older texts may cause confusion, but we emphasise that this is an ongoing process, so some of the names used in this guide will inevitably change in due course.

Some animals benefit, of course, from English names. We have included many of these where they are well established, but we caution that these can never be as definitive as the names in the formal classification, even if they do tend to change less!

A complete list of the animals covered by this guide, and their classification, is given at the end of the book (pages 184-192).

Geographical scope of the book

This guide is designed to allow identification of the freshwater invertebrates that occur in Britain, Ireland and their associated smaller islands, including the Channel Islands. In most cases, it will also suffice to identify those invertebrates that occur in the adjacent parts of mainland Europe, although keys that take identification beyond family level may not work so effectively. Outside the lowland regions of western Europe, however, its use will become more limited, and it omits many groups that occur in the Mediterranean region.

There are a few distinctive families on the European mainland adjacent to Britain that have not crossed the English Channel. Most notable are the mayfly (Ephemeroptera) family Polymitarcidae and the prawn (Crustacea) family Atyidae; both are mentioned in the appropriate keys.

The changing freshwater fauna of Britain and Ireland

The fauna of a water body changes over time. Sometimes this is because the quality of the water changes, causing some species intolerant of the change to become locally extinct whilst others adapted to the new conditions move in and colonise. On a more geographical scale, however, there are also changes occurring. Some species may have become extinct, such as the orange spotted emerald dragonfly (*Oxygastra curtisii*), last seen in England in 1957, and there are certainly species that are increasingly becoming restricted in distribution and even moving towards extinction throughout the country: the freshwater pearl mussel (*Margaritifera margaritifera*) and the white-clawed crayfish (*Austropotamobius pallipes*) are good examples, but there are less obvious ones such as the stonefly *Isogenus nubecula*, not seen in Britain now for some decades despite considerable effort to find it.

At the same time, previously unrecorded species are occasionally found. Normally, these are animals that have simply been overlooked, but there may be examples of natural colonisation, particularly of flying insects. Some of our dragonflies and damselflies (Odonata) with southerly distributions are expanding their ranges northwards and, as these are active fliers as adults, it may be that new species establish from mainland Europe in due course.

More commonly, however, new species are added through human introduction, occasionally deliberate but usually accidental. Introductions have not only added new species, but also new genera and even the occasional new family (and Entoprocta, if it arrives, will be an entirely new phylum composed mostly of sessile aquatic organisms). A major source of introductions is the Ponto-Caspian Region, covering the areas around the Black and Caspian Seas, from which many species have expanded, generally through ballast water in ships, across Europe and even beyond. Some Ponto-Caspian invaders have been around in Britain for many years, including the zebra mussel (*Dreissena polymorpha*), which arrived in the 19th century; the most recent arrival, the shrimp *Dikerogammarus villosus*, turned up only in 2010. Other invaders come from North America, including the crayfish *Pacifastacus lenuisculus* and *Procambarus clarkii*. Most of these invasives have probably arrived in Britain following establishment in western Europe (and then moved on to Ireland from Britain), but Britain has reciprocated in recent years by exporting the American shrimp *Crangonyx pseudogracilis* to the adjacent parts of Europe.

Not all introductions have come from so far away as the Black Sea or North America. A more local example is that of the shrimp *Gammarus pulex*, native to Britain but not to Ireland or the Isle of Man, to both of which it was deliberately introduced in the 20th century. Although native to one part of the region, this species, when introduced outside its natural range, has had a detrimental effect on the native fauna in the same way that so many invasives from outside the region have done, and is a cautionary tale about the dangers of translocating freshwater animals.

Studying freshwater organisms

Collecting freshwater invertebrates

It is easy to pursue freshwater studies, as all types of water body, bar the most ephemeral of rain puddles, are potentially fruitful sources of invertebrates. Relatively little equipment is needed, although the following are recommended. A net is always useful; hand searching, by lifting stones, for example, and examining what is attached or clinging to them, can be fruitful, but a net will help to catch those animals with the power to swim or crawl away. This does not have to be particularly fancy: a kitchen sieve can be very effective for sweeping through submerged vegetation or holding downstream while you dislodge stream sediment with your hands or feet. It is also useful to have a high sided tray which you can fill with water before depositing the contents of your net; animals caught in a net will often remain very still, and only once immersed in water will they move and become visible to you. You will need containers into which to place the animals you find; if you are keeping your specimens alive, remember that certain predatory animals will attack and eat others, so keep them separate. Finally, you will need implements to pick animals out of the net or tray: fingers are fine for some animals, but forceps (tweezers) and teaspoons are needed for particularly small or fast-moving ones. Remember also to carry some means of labelling your containers; labels written in pencil that are then placed inside the containers are best, particularly if you have access to waterproof paper. Writing on the outside of containers with permanent markers is also good (do this before the container gets wet), but remember if you are using any alcohol-based preservative that the ink is soluble in alcohol.

You may be interested only in examining live animals, but in much identification it is more practical if the animal is killed. Hard-bodied arthropods (insects, arachnids and crustaceans) can be killed by immersion in alcohol. An alternative is to immerse it in very hot water (c. 80°C) , which causes almost instantaneous death. This is recommended for Diptera larvae with retractable heads, so that their bodies remain extended, but of course is not practical in the field so requires carrying animals home alive.

13

Wherever you collect animals, always remember two vitally important points. First, always consider safety: water bodies of all types hold dangers, from risk of drowning in deep water or becoming stuck in wetland mud, to the annoyance of biting insects and the disease-carrying potential of contaminated water. Be aware of potential hazards, take precautions and avoid unnecessary risks. Second, only collect where you have permission to do so, and minimise any damage caused by the collecting process. Bear in mind that several freshwater invertebrates are protected, including freshwater pearl mussel (p46) and white-clawed crayfish (p86), making intentional killing, injuring or collecting illegal.

Preserving and storing invertebrates

Most freshwater invertebrates are best preserved submerged in alcohol. A mixture of 70% ethanol and 30% water is the best all round medium, but methylated spirits diluted to the same concentration is a suitable alternative and, at a pinch, surgical spirits or even vodka are useful!

Always ensure that preserved specimens are appropriately labelled. The date and location of collection are crucial, the latter as precise as possible and ideally including a grid reference. Notes on habitat type are useful. Once identified, the name of the person making the identification should be added to the label.

Equipment needed to identify organisms

For identification you will need some form of magnification. A hand lens can be useful in some situations, but normally you will need a microscope. We have ensured that the keys in this book will normally work without a high level of magnification (x40 should suffice in most cases), but for most of the invertebrates in this book you will need one with a good distance between the specimen and the lens (a so-called 'dissecting' microscope); this is to allow a three dimensional object to be viewed. Some very small animals, such as rotifers and the smaller crustaceans, are better examined using a 'stage microscope' (the type with a platform for slides). Whatever microscope you have, lighting is critical: with a dissecting microscope you need to be able to illuminate your specimen from above and, ideally, be able to move the lighting so that you can illuminate from different angles. Stage microscopes require illumination from below, but this will almost certainly be built in to the microscope itself.

Along with the microscope, you will need various other pieces of equipment. Petri dishes are clear plastic or glass containers, normally 50-80 mm in diameter and 10 mm deep, that are extremely useful for examining specimens under the dissecting microscope. Most larger invertebrates are best examined while immersed in alcohol or water, as this removes the problem of glare of lights on wet surfaces and also provides support, so features such as gills do not 'slump', and petri dishes provide the container in which this liquid can be held. Microscope slides and coverslips are equally useful for stage microscopes.

Forceps are essential to handle specimens, and it pays to invest in at least one pair of very fine watchmakers' or surgical forceps with needle-like points. Needles mounted on a long handle are also useful. For very small organisms, pipettes can be very valuable; these are simple glass tubes with a very narrow end for picking up animals and a compressible rubber bung for creating a vacuum to enable specimens to be sucked into the pipette.

The best way of getting hold of the equipment needed, if you do not have access to a laboratory, is to go to a specialist entomological supplier, who will be able to supply equipment in the small quantities that an amateur naturalist will require. Some suppliers are listed on the FBA website.

How this book is organised

This guide uses a series of identification keys, starting with an introductory key to enable you to determine the main group to which your animal belongs and continuing with a series of more detailed keys to specific groups. Working through the keys will take you to an end point that should be achievable without the requirement for dissection, specialist equipment or high magnification.

Using the keys

This guide is based mainly on dichotomous keys, meaning that at each point you are given a choice of two options, which either lead you to another numbered couplet or to an end point.

Starting at number 1 in the key, decide which of the two choices listed under that number applies to the animal you have. On the right hand side, there will be either a number or a name. If there is a number, move straight to the couplet with that number and repeat the procedure. So, if you have a free-living animal and are at couplet 1 of Key A, it directs you to go straight to couplet 4, without having to consider the intervening couplets 2 and 3. Continue in this way until you reach an end point: the name of an animal. The keys include various end points, depending on the ease of identification; some end points are of entire phyla, whereas others are for individual species. Most are, however, to family or genus.

Some couplet numbers include a second number in parentheses, e.g. 4(1). This second number shows the couplet in the key from which you were directed (in this case, couplet 1) to where you are now (in this case, couplet 4). This is useful to allow you to follow your progress, and to backtrack if you realise you have made a mistake. If you were directed from the previous couplet in the key, then there will be no second number in parentheses.

Sometimes, a 'couplet' will give you a choice of three or four options; if there are more than two choices, this will be made clear at the beginning of the 'couplet'. However many choices you have at any given point, your animal should only fit one of the options.

At certain points you may come to a name along with a number (or, in Keys A and F, reference to a later key in the book). This shows that you have identified your specimen to a particular group, such as family, but that the key will now allow you to go further in your identification. If there is no further number, the key has reached an end point. Sometimes, the end point will include the word 'part' (for example, couplet 3 in Key A includes 'Phylum CNIDARIA – part'); this means that the particular taxonomic group at which you have arrived (in this case Cnidaria), has other representatives that will key out elsewhere.

Throughout the keys we have included illustrations. Sometimes these illustrate specific features, but mostly they are to give a general idea of what the animal should look like. Bear in mind, however, that the illustrations are usually of particular species, whereas most of the end points will encompass more than one species, so your specimen may not be exactly the same as that illustrated. Where a whole animal is illustrated, it is always shown with the anterior (front or 'head' end) towards the left or top, unless otherwise stated. Where helpful, the figure caption will tell you if it is shown in dorsal (from above), ventral (from below) or lateral (from the side) view. The figures are not to scale, so always check the approximate size ranges given at the end point, rather than comparing with another figure.

Where a couplet refers to a figure, remember that the illustration is part of the identification process: if you do not understand what feature or characteristic the text is describing, a look at the illustration should provide assistance.

It is useful to examine the illustrations in advance of using the keys, in order to get an idea of what your specimen may be, but this tentative identification should always be followed by working through the key, as some critical features may not be immediately obvious until the text points them out to you.

The Glossary

We have often used specialist terms with which you may not be familiar. Where these are first used, we have included a brief explanation of meaning and, in addition, a glossary at the end provides definitions of technical terms.

When you reach an end point

Different taxonomic groups are identified to different levels, depending upon their diversity and complexity. Where we refer to a genus or species as an intermediate or end point, you will be able to identify that by its being written in italics; a family, subfamily or tribe is recognisable by the ending of its name: 'idae', 'inae' or 'ini'. For higher levels in the taxonomic hierarchy, we have specified its level (e.g. order, class or phylum) and used capital letters for the name itself.

For every end point we have given the following information, unless it appears elsewhere in the key.

a) Expected maximum size. All animals can of course be smaller than the maximum, but maximum size can be a helpful hint in identification. Do not take these too literally: there will inevitably be individuals that exceed this. However, if we give the maximum length of an organism as 5 mm, you may well come across one that is 6 mm long, but if it is 16 mm long, you have probably made a mistake in your identification!

b) Number of freshwater families, genera and species contained within it that have been recorded from Britain, so that you are aware of the diversity that each contains.

c) An idea of habitat in which it occurs. Again, we have given the most common habitat, but occasionally animals turn up in the 'wrong' place so do not use this as a definitive indicator of identification.

d) Any other information that may be useful in identifying your animal, and any important name changes, to help in cross-referencing with other guides.

Key A – Main groups of invertebrates

Acari

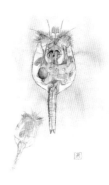

Rotifera

This key covers all types of freshwater invertebrates and is the place to start if you have no idea, or are unsure, of the type of animal you are trying to identify. In most cases you will be referred to later keys, but it does include some end points. Many of the end points in this key are of phyla, which may be very diverse but are difficult to identify further without specialist preparation and equipment.

The Key

1   Organism firmly attached to a surface, either in the form of an encrustation, or a series of branching tubes, or a mat-like tangle, or jelly-like—   **2**

—   Animal free-living, either crawling, burrowing, temporarily attached, or free-swimming—   **4**

2   Irregular encrustation, sometimes with protruding 'fingers', rough to
     the touch and with many tiny perforations (fig. A1)—

Phylum PORIFERA (sponges)

Encrustations can exceed 100 mm across, but normally smaller; up to 20 mm are
more common. 1 family (Spongillidae); 4 genera; 5 species. Grey or greenish in
colour, growing on stones, branches and other solid surfaces in clean water.
Common, but easily overlooked. Die off over winter, surviving as small dormant
structures called gemules.

a)
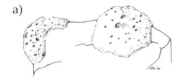

b)

Fig. A1. Porifera (sponges): (a) encrusting growth of entire organisms on a stone;
(b) detail of surface, showing small spine-like structures (spicules).

—   Distinct tubes, often branching and ending in tentacles—   **3**

3   Animal colonial, consisting of branching horny tubes enclosing soft
     living tissue that extends outside them and terminates in numerous
     tentacle-bearing 'heads', or as a jelly-like mass from which similar
     tentacle-bearing heads protrude (fig. A2)—

Phylum BRYOZOA (bryozoans)

Colonies usually more than 10 mm
across, with each individual (or
zooid) up to 4 mm long. 6 families;
7 genera; 11 species. Also known as
Ectoprocta. Attach to solid substrata
in clean water, particularly branches
and roots and normally in the shade.
Common, but easily overlooked.
Die off in winter, surviving as
small disc-like structures called
statoblasts.

Fig. A2. Portion of a Bryozoan colony.

The phylum Entoprocta may key out here. This has stalks consisting of bead-like segments growing from a single plate attached to the substratum, with a cup at the end surrounded by non-retractable tentacles. It is up to 4 mm long. The single species, *Urnatella gracilis*, is not recorded from Britain, but may have been overlooked; there have been occasional northern European records, which are probably introductions from North America.

—   Body soft, cylindrical, attached to a surface at one end (although able to detach and move), the other end terminating in a circlet of 5-13 extensible tentacles (fig. A3a)—   **Phylum CNIDARIA - part**

Hydra - 2 families; 2 genera; 5 species. The familiar green hydra is one of four species of *Hydra* (family Hydridae), which can be up to 50 mm long when fully extended, though normally less than 20 mm long; it is common and widely distributed in all kinds of still water bodies. *Cordylophora caspia*, the only freshwater member of the family Clavidae, grows in branching colonies up to 60 mm tall, its main stalk enclosed in a chitinous tube; a 19th century Ponto-Caspian introduction, it is localised and rare, its main stronghold being the Norfolk Broads (notes continued overleaf).

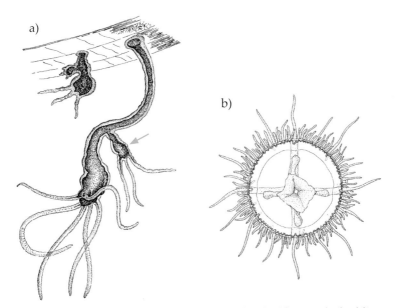

Fig. A3. Cnidaria: (a) *Hydra* sp., showing new individual forming by budding (arrowed); (b) medusa of *Craspedacusta sowerbii*.

A third family, Protohydridae, with one species (*Protohydra leuckarti*), occurs in brackish water and may occasionally stray into coastal fresh water.
Note: some members of the phylum Rotifera attach themselves to solid substratum. They are distinguishable from hydra in lacking tentacles, instead having a distinct circle of cilia (fig. A4); see couplet 5.

4(1)   Circular in shape, soft-bodied and transparent with tentacles
(fig. A3b)—   **Phylum CNIDARIA - part**

Jellyfish - up to 25 mm in diameter. 1 species: *Craspedacusta sowerbii*, often mis-spelt *C. sowerbyi* (family Olindiidae). Still waters. Introduced from China, populations rarely persist for very long and the distinctive circular form, known as the medusa, will only be seen after a long spell of warm weather. The life cycle of *C. sowerbii* includes a far less conspicuous polyp stage.

—   Without the above combination of characters—   **5**

5   Anterior end bearing a circle of cilia (tiny whip-like structures) that in life gives the impression of a rotating wheel; form variable, cuticle or skin either very thin and flexible or thickened to form a stiff shell (known as a lorica) (fig. A4)—   **Phylum ROTIFERA (rotifers)**

Always very small, usually less than 1 mm long. 27 families; 94 genera; nearly 500 species. Most species are free-swimming or crawl in sediment or on vegetation; fixed forms are generally attached to vegetation, although some attach to larger invertebrates. When viewed live, the circle of continuously moving cilia is very distinctive.

Fig. A4. Rotifera. Examples of different rotifer body forms in lateral view.

—   Without the above combination of characters—   **6**

6   Body generally elongate and forked at the hind end; cuticle covered with minute bristles, sometimes scales (fig. A5)—
     Phylum GASTROTRICHA (gastrotrichs or hairy backs)

Less than 1 mm long. 4 families; 11 genera; more than 50 species. Occur on the surface layer of plants and organic sediments; mainly in standing waters. They are also frequently part of the interstitial fauna. Non-swimming, but use rows of cilia to move by gliding.

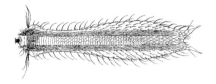

Fig. A5. Gastrotricha, dorsal view.

—   Without the above combination of characters—   **7**

7   With a calcareous shell into which the soft parts can contract, single (as in snails) or bivalve (as in mussels); body soft and unsegmented—
     Phylum MOLLUSCA: Key D (p40)

—   Without a calcareous shell, although a carapace may be present—   **8**

Note: This next 'couplet' has three end points

8   Body with distinctive segments; jointed limbs and/or distinct segmented antennae usually present; a tough/hard exoskeleton may be present, covering all or part of the body and often pigmented—
     Phylum ARTHROPODA: 9

Diptera (true flies) belong here. Diptera larvae lack jointed legs and some may have a worm-like appearance; none, however, has more than 14 body segments.

—   Segmented or unsegmented, generally worm-like body without jointed limbs or segmented antennae; usually long and slender or flattened; no hard exoskeleton; eyes may be present; suckers may be present at one or both ends of the body—   **11**

—   Very small, stout-bodied animal with four pairs of prolegs, each terminating in several claws (fig. A6)—
     Phylum TARDIGRADA (tardigades or water bears)

Normally less than 1mm long. 3 families; 4 genera; 42 species. Specialist inhabitants of mosses and algae, and common where this habitat occurs. They are able to withstand drying and so will occur where moss is seasonally wet.

Fig. A6. Tardigrada, lateral view.

Note: This next 'couplet' has three end points

9   Four pairs of jointed legs; head, thorax and often abdomen not clearly separated; antennae absent— **Class ARACHNIDA: 10**

—   Three pairs of jointed legs, or none, and normally a distinct head; larvae without jointed legs may have prolegs; one pair of antennae, although often very small and indistinct— **Classes INSECTA (true insects) and ENTOGNATHA (springtails): Key F (p72)**

Note. Small immature mites (Class Arachnida) have three pairs of legs. They are always very small (less than 1mm long), with the head and thorax not distinctly separated.

—   Number of jointed legs variable (but never three pairs); often with appendages on the abdomen; body either enclosed in a bivalve carapace, with or without a hinge OR body with a single thoracic carapace OR body without a carapace; two pairs of antennae— **Class CRUSTACEA: Key E (p48)**

10   Body divided into two parts: prosoma (head and thorax) and opisthosoma (abdomen) (fig. A7)— **Order ARANEAE (spiders)**

Fig. A7. Araneae: the water spider, *Argyroneta aquatica*, dorsal view.

Up to 25 mm long. The water spider *Argyroneta aquatica* (Cybaeidae) (fig. A7) is the only truly aquatic spider. It creates a home filled with air amongst aquatic vegetation. It is uniformly dark and thickly covered with tiny hairs, which trap air, and when under water its abdomen appears silvery, due to this layer of air. It carries air from the surface in this way to fill its retreat.

The raft spider *Dolomedes fimbriatus* (Pisauridae) is not truly aquatic but always lives in association with water and may be seen running across the water surface; it has two broad pale stripes along its body. Many terrestrial spiders occur in riparian and emergent vegetation, including specialist inhabitants of marsh plants, and are frequently encountered in samples, as the sampling process dislodges them. The hunting spider *Pirata piscatorius* (Lycosidae) lives on *Sphagnum* bog and creates a burrow into the moss which often extends below the water line.

— Body not divided: prosoma completely fused to opisthosoma (fig. A8)—
Order ACARI (mites)

Up to 2 mm long and often bright red in colour. Mites are common in many freshwater environments and extremely diverse, with 30 families, 73 genera and over 300 species. Mites found in fresh water belong to either the Halacaridae (fig. A8a) or the Hydrachnidea (also known as Hydrachnellae or Hydracarina) (fig. A8b). Halacarids are chiefly marine but freshwater species are found in lakes, streams, wells, cave pools and the interstitial habitat. Although diverse in their distribution, Halacaridae are morphologically remarkably similar. The majority of mites found in fresh water belong to the Hydrachnidia, and unlike the Halacaridae are extremely diverse in their morphology.

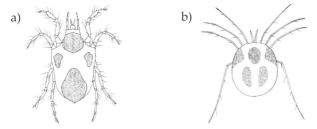

Fig. A8. Acari (mites) in dorsal view: (a) Halacaridae; (b) Hydrachnidea.

11(8) Body divided into clear segments—
Phylum ANNELIDA (segmented or true worms): Key C (p33)

It is possible to mistake some Diptera larvae (Class Insecta) for annelids. Diptera are insects, with hardened mouthparts. Many have an obvious head, but some can retract this into the thorax so it may not be visible, whilst others have a vestigial head capsule. Diptera will not have more than 14 body segments, whilst most annelids have considerably more than this. Diptera larvae without hardened heads never have suckers and are non-swimming. If you suspect you have a Diptera larva, proceed to Key F (page 72).

—   Body not segmented—   **12**

12   Body cylindrical—   **13**

—   Body flattened—   **14**

13   Body tapers at each end; covered with a tough but flexible and usually transparent cuticle (fig. A9)—   **Phylum NEMATODA (nematodes)**

Up to 3 mm long. 18 families; 31 genera; 70 species. Debris in standing and slow-flowing water; also many terrestrial species common in wet soil. Some can swim, but all move with quite a stiff thrashing motion. Some are internal parasites of aquatic insects.

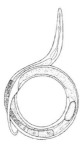
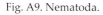
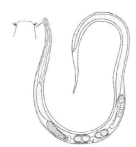

Fig. A9. Nematoda.

— Body blunt-ended; cuticle opaque (fig. A10)—
Phylum NEMATOMORPHA (horsehair worms)

At least 20 mm and up to 200 mm. 2 families; 3 genera; 4 species. Ponds, ditches and wetlands. Very slender, normally less than 1 mm in diameter. Internal parasites of insects as larvae, only the short-lived adult stage being free-living in water, so rarely encountered. Movement is quite stiff, unlike the large undulations of segmented worms (oligochaetes, phylum Annelida). Also known as Gordian worms.

Fig. A10. Nematomorpha (horsehair worm).

14(12) Animal with a long proboscis, contained at rest in a cavity in the body but extendable beyond the front of the head; 4-8 eyespots in pairs, normally 6 arranged in 3 pairs; posterior end tapering—
Phylum NEMERTEA (ribbon worms or proboscis worms)

Up to 20 mm long. 1 family: Tetrastemmatidae; 1 genus: *Prostoma*; 2 species. Standing and slow-flowing water in vegetation. Non-swimming but use rows of cilia to move by gliding. Rarely encountered and poorly known.

— Body conspicuously flattened, with 2, 3, 4 or many eyespots; if many eyespots, these form a border at anterior (front) end; no proboscis; posterior end bluntly rounded—
Class TURBELLARIA (flatworms): Key B (p28)

Key B – Turbellaria

(Flatworms)

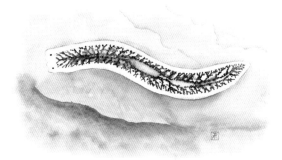

Dendrocoelum lacteum

The Turbellaria is a class within the phylum Platyhelminthes, which also includes parasitic forms such as flukes (class Trematoda), tapeworms (class Cestoda) and monogeneans (class Monogenea), some of which have a brief free-living aquatic stage as they move between host animals.

This key only covers the larger flatworms, in the order Tricladida (triclads). There are also more than 50 species of Microturbellaria, most of which are up to 3 mm long, although some can reach 12 mm; they are found in a wide variety of freshwater habitats and many can tolerate brackish water.

There are three families of triclads. The various genera do not key out simply into families, so all genera and species are keyed out or mentioned in the key. Identification is mainly by general body shape and location of eyes, but some may require examination of the pharynx, the anterior part of the digestive system which is, however, normally visible through the body wall and therefore does not require any dissection.

Try to examine flatworms live, if possible, as killing and preservation normally reduces them to jelly-like structures which, to the non-expert, can easily be overlooked as being an animal, and on which identification features are almost impossible to see. Live animals move relatively slowly and their identification features will be clearly visible.

The Key

Note: all figures show animals in dorsal view.

1   Many eyes arranged in a border around the head (fig. B1)—
Planariidae: *Polycelis*

Up to 12 mm long. 3 species. *Polycelis felina* is found on the under-surface of stones and plants in small streams, *P. nigra* in lowland streams and lakes and *P. tenuis* in quieter stretches of streams and rivers but especially characteristic of lakes and ponds.

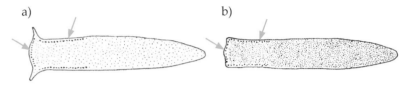

a)   b)

Fig. B1. Planariidae with multiple eyes arrowed: (a) *Polycelis felina*, a clearly tentacled form; (b) *Polycelis nigra*, without tentacles but with a blunt-edge head.

—   Two eyes (occasionally three or four)—   **2**

2   Body not pigmented and white in colour (food in gut may give an appearance of colour)—   **3**

—   Body pigmented—   **4**

3   Eyes well separated; when live, head with slight development of
     tentacles (fig. B2) —   **Dendrocoelidae:** *Dendrocoelum lacteum*

     Up to 25 mm long. Fairly common, especially in productive lakes.

Fig. B2. Dendrocoelidae: *Dendrocoelum lacteum*, with widely spaced eyes
(arrowed).

—   Eyes close together; head blunt-edged with no indication of tentacles
     (fig. B3) —   **Planariidae:** *Phagocata vitta*

     Up to 12 mm long. Typical of high, peaty ground, in cool streams, lakes,
     groundwater and springs.

Fig. B3. Planariidae: *Phagocata vitta*, with eyes close together (arrowed).

4(2) Blunt-edged head clearly narrower than body; distinct anterior sucker
      (fig. B4) —   **Dendrocoelidae:** *Bdellocephala punctata*

      Up to 35 mm long. Lakes and canals: usually on under-surface of stones but can
      also live on vegetation.

Fig. B4. Dendrocoelidae: *Bdellocephala punctata*.

—   Head similar in width or wider than body —   **5**

Note: This has three end points.

5   Head triangular or round-edged ('spatulate') (fig. B5) —   **Dugesiidae**

Up to 25 mm long. 1 genus: *Dugesia*; 3 species. *Dugesia lugubris* and *D. polychora* are found on the under-surfaces of stones and vegetation in mineral rich lakes, but also in the quieter reaches of streams and rivers, the latter being the more common of the two. *Dugesia tigrina* is found in running and still waters, including lakes, though is absent from unproductive waters,.

a)   b)

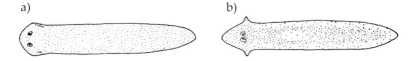

Fig. B5. Dugesiidae: (a) *Dugesia polychroa*, (b) *Dugesia tigrina*.

—   Head with awl-shaped tentacles (fig. B6) —

Planariidae: *Crenobia alpina*

Up to 12 mm long. Under-surfaces of stones, characteristically in springs and small, cool, swiftly flowing streams.

Fig. B6. Planariidae: *Crenobia alpina*.

—   Head blunt-edged —   **6**

6   Pharynx as seen from the dorsal surface is branched (polypharyngeal)
     (fig. B7)—   **Planariidae: *Phagocata woodworthi***

Up to 16 mm long. A North American species introduced to Loch Ness.

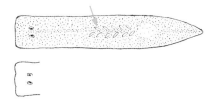

Fig. B7. Planariidae: *Phagocata woodworthi*, above whole animal, with branched
pharynx arrowed; below shows an alternative anterior end which may be
encountered.

—   Pharynx a single structure without branches—
                                        Planariidae: *Planaria torva* (fig. B8)

Up to 12 mm long. Found on the under-surfaces of stones and plants in all types
of freshwater habitats.

Fig. B8. Planariidae: *Planaria torva*.

Key C – Annelida

(Leeches and true worms)

Glossiphoniidae

Freshwater annelids divide into four main groups: the widespread and diverse Oligochaeta (true worms) and Hirudinea (leeches), and the more restricted Polychaeta and Branchiobdellida. Technically, Polychaeta are a separate class, while the other three are subclasses of the class Clitellaria. All have bodies clearly divided into multiple segments, with few other external features.

The structures used to distinguish families of leeches are straightforward, if occasionally somewhat difficult to see. The body tends to be narrower towards the front, with a small sucker at the end, and wider towards the back, with a large sucker at the end (fig. C1a,b). At the front end on the dorsal side are the eyes, normally visible as small dark spots (fig. C2a-c). The main problem arises if the specimen is very dark and the eyes are not, therefore, clearly visible.

Identification of oligochaetes is based heavily on the chaetae, the small hair-like or hook-like features found on most of the body segments. Unfortunately, these are usually extremely small and require high magnification. They grow in regularly arranged bundles on the body segments (fig. C3). Diagnostic features are: the number of chaetae in each bundle, whether there are short chaetae only or two clearly distinct lengths of chaetae (the longer ones being known as hair chaetae; e.g. fig. C9), and whether the chaetae are single-pointed or have two or more points at the end. There are normally four bundles per segment: two ventral and two dorso-lateral.

Begin identification of aquatic oligochaetes by making sure which end is which. The anterior end is thicker than the posterior end; the very front is the location of a rounded (or sometimes proboscis-like) lobe called the prostomium (e.g. fig. C8, C9). See if there is a clitellum, the swollen area in which the sexual organs are situated, which is always towards the front of the animal if present, but is often absent; note that worms are hermaphrodite (both sexes in one individual) so if sexually mature a male pore will always be present, although as this is a small hole in one of the segments it is difficult to see. Segments are numbered from front to rear, normally using Roman numerals (I, IV, XI, etc.) but for simplicity of use we use standard numbering in the key below.

When examining oligochaetes remember that any reference to colour should only be applied to live animals, and that preserved specimens of many species will break into pieces very easily.

This key should work for most animals, but among the oligochaetes there are a few aberrant species, introduced families and groundwater specialists that we have excluded.

The key

Note: This next 'couplet' has three end points

1   Body with suckers at both the anterior and posterior ends. No obvious head structure—   **Subclass HIRUDINEA (leeches): 2**

—   Body with a sucker at the posterior end only; first four segments fused to form a head—   **Subclass BRANCHIOBDELLIDA** (fig. C4)

Up to 5 mm long. 1 species: *Branchiobdella astaci*. Parasitic on crayfish.

—   Body lacking suckers—   **5**

2   2-8 eyes, if 8 then placed longitudinally (fig. C2a)—
                                                             Order RHYNCHOBDELLIDA: 3

—   8 or 10 eyes, if 8 then placed transversely (fig. C2b)—
                                                           Order ARHYNCHOBDELLIDA: 4

3   Body depressed/flattened; indistinct anterior sucker (fig. C1a)—
Glossiphoniidae

Typically up to 25 mm long at rest, although *Placobdella costata* reaches 70mm at rest. 6 genera; 8 species. Most water types.

—   Body cylindrical; both suckers distinct (fig. C1b)—   **Piscicolidae**

Up to 30 mm long at rest. 1 species: *Piscicola geometra* (fish leech). Widespread where fish are present.

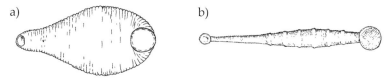

a)   b)

Fig. C1. Examples of leeches in ventral view: (a) *Glossiphonia complanata* (Glossiphoniidae); (b) *Piscicola geometra* (Piscicolidae).

4(2) 10 eyes; 5 pairs arranged in a crescent around edge of head (fig. C2c)—
Hirudinidae

Up to 60 mm long at rest. 2 genera; 2 species. Eyes may be hard to see due to dark pigmentation of body. Found in still and slow flowing waters. The two species are the horse leech (*Haemopsis sanguisuga*), which is a predator of small animals and unable to pierce the skin of large mammals, and the extremely rare medicinal leech (*Hirudo medicinalis*), so named because it can pierce human skin and has been used in bloodletting for medicinal purposes.

—   8 eyes, 4 pairs arranged in two transverse rows (fig. C2b)—
Erpobdellidae

Up to 30 mm long at rest. 3 genera; 5 species. All types of fresh waters, abundant in highly enriched waters.

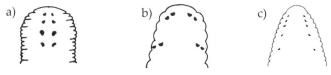

a)   b)   c)

Fig. C2. Arrangement of leech eyes: (a) longitudinally; (b) transversely; (c) arranged in a crescent around edge of head.

5(1)   Hair chaetae present in both dorsal and ventral bundles—
                                          Class POLYCHAETA (fig. C5)

Polychaeta are mostly marine, and include familiar species such as ragworm (*Hediste diversicolor*) which occasionally turns up in coastal rivers. There is also one family – the Aeolosomatidae – with truly freshwater representatives in the genus *Aeolosoma*. These are tiny, rarely more than 5 mm long, with a distinctly rounded prostomium that is wider than the rest of the body and with tiny coloured spots over the body.

—   Hair chaetae absent, or confined to dorsal bundles. Dorsal bundles may be absent—   **Subclass OLIGOCHAETA: 6**

The families covered by this key are in two orders. The family Lumbriculidae is in the order Lumbriculida; the remainder are in the order Haplotaxida.

6   Chaetae one per bundle in all bundles—   **Haplotaxidae**

Long thread-like worms up to 300 mm long. 1 species: *Haplotaxis gordioides* (fig. C6). Found in cooler surface water, groundwater and wet soil.

—   Chaetae two or more per bundle—   **7**

7   Chaetae two per bundle in all bundles—   **8**

—   Number of chaetae variable, usually more than 2 (2 per bundle may be present but never on all bundles)—   **10**

8   When live, white in colour; all chaetae single-pointed (as in fig. C3d,e); male pore and beginning of clitellum (if present) on segment 12—
                                          Enchytraeidae - part

Up to 20 mm long. 9 genera; 25 species. Family mainly terrestrial, but some species live in detritus and mud under water.

—   When live, pink or darker worms—   **9**

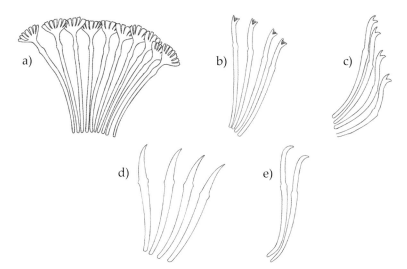

Fig. C3. Examples of oligochaete chaetae: (a) palmate; (b) pectinate; (c) bifid; (d) (e) single-pointed.

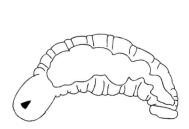

Fig. C4. Branchiobdellida, ventral view.

Fig. C5. Aeolosomatidae, dorsal view.

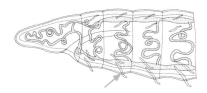

Fig. C6. Haplotaxidae: *Haplotaxis gordioides*, anterior end in lateral view showing single chaeta (arrowed).

9   Animal earthworm-like, usually several centimetres long and several millimetres thick; chaetae single-pointed—
Lumbricidae (fig. C7) and **Sparganophilidae**

Lumbricidae (earthworms) normally only occur accidentally in water, but 9 species in 7 genera appear to be semi-aquatic. Sparganophilidae has 1 species: *Sparganophilus tamesis*, found in margins of lakes and rivers. The families can be distinguished if sexually mature. In Lumbricidae the male pores are paired and on segment 15 (seldom on 13 or 14) with the clitellum further towards rear, not beginning before segment 20. In Sparganophilidae the clitellum starts on segment 14 to 16 and covers the male pores which are on segment 19.

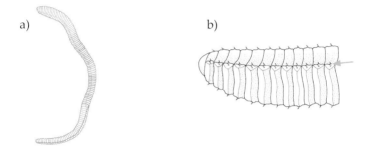

a)   b)

Fig. C7. Lumbricidae: (a) whole animal; (b) anterior end in lateral view with chaetae in pairs arrowed.

—   Long thin worms; chaetae single-pointed or bifid (double- pointed as in fig. C3c); in mature specimens, male pores and front end of clitellum usually on segment 8, 9 or 10 (occasionally on 7 or 11)— **Lumbriculidae**

Up to 80 mm long. 6 genera; 10 species. A range of habitats, including rivers; can swim well.

10(7) Chaetae mostly bifid (some bundles may have single-pointed chaetae); hair chaetae present or absent—   **11**

—   When live, white in colour; all chaetae single-pointed; male pore and beginning of clitellum on segment 12—   **Enchytraeidae - part**

Note: This next 'couplet' has three end points

11 When live, white in colour; chaetae 3-4 per bundle and uniformly bifid; male pore and beginning of clitellum on segment 12 —   **Propappidae**

Up to 12 mm long. 1 species *Propappus volki* (fig. C8), in rivers and sandy lake shores.

a)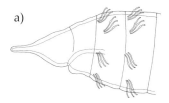

b)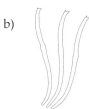

Fig. C8. *Proppappus volki* (Propappidae): (a) anterior of animal; (b) detail of bundle of chaetae.

— When live, pale and translucent in colour; chaetae mostly bifid; male pore on segment 5, 6 or 7 —   **Naididae**

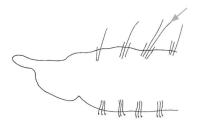

Normally less than 10 mm long. 14 genera; 33 species. May have hair chaetae (fig. C9). Generally reproduce asexually, by budding, so the clitellum is rarely present. Found especially on water plants, also in sediment of water bodies. The genus *Pristina* is considered by some to be in a separate family, the Pristinidae.

Fig. C9. *Naididae*: *Pristina* sp., anterior end, showing long dorsal hair chaetae (arrowed).

— When live, red to pink in colour; chaetae normally more than 2 per bundle and mostly bifid; hair chaetae often present; in mature worms, male pores and front end of clitellum on segment 11 (rarely on 10, 8 or 7, exceptionally on 12) —   **Tubificidae**

Up to 70 mm long. 17 genera; 36 species. Fine sediment, often in heavily polluted areas. Unable to swim and if disturbed will coil tightly and continuously.

Key D – Mollusca

(Snails, limpets and mussels)

Radix balthica

All freshwater molluscs have shells, whose structure is used in identification. Shape and relative dimension of shells is important. There are three fundamental shell types (fig. D1): cone-shaped, spiral and bivalve. For each, relative measures of shell length and height may be important diagnostic features, while for cone-shaped and bivalve shells, shell breadth is also useful. These dimensions are shown on fig. D1.

Identification of gastropods requires determination of the presence or otherwise of an operculum. This is a horny or calcified plate which the animal carries on its back when extended and which closes the aperture (opening) of the shell when the animal is retracted. Pay particular care with small specimens, as it may be necessary to prod within the aperture with a pin or fine forceps to determine the presence/absence of an operculum. Snails possessing an operculum are referred to as operculate.

Shells can last long after the animal has died and its soft parts have decomposed; they can even persist in sediments for thousands of years. Therefore, it is important to confirm that living specimens are present if you are making identification from empty shells. Be aware also that an empty shell may represent an animal that once had an operculum, which will have since disappeared.

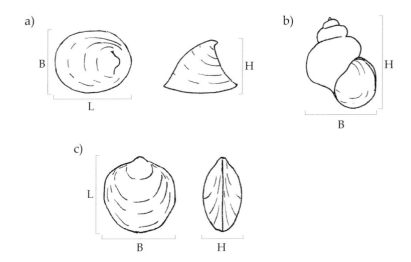

Fig. D1. Dimensions of mollusc shells, showing length, L, breadth, B, and height, H: (a) cone-shaped shells; (b) spiral shells; (c) bivalve shells.

The Key

1 Shell, coiled (snail-like) or oval and pointed (limpet-like)—
Class GASTROPODA (snails and limpets): 2

— Shell in two parts (bivalve) joined by a hinge (mussel-like)—
Class BIVALVIA (mussels): 11

2 Shell with no obvious coiling (limpet-like) (fig. D1a & D2)— **3**

— Shell coiled— **4**

3   Shell length at least 2x height and breadth; shell apex (pointed top) inclined to the left (view from above) (fig. D2a)—   **Acroloxidae**

Up to 7 mm long. 1 species: *Acroloxus lacustris*. Common in lakes, ponds and streams, though not found in very fast water. Associated with plants. The introduced *Ferrissia clessiniana* (Planorbidae) looks like *Acroloxus* but has a shell apex that inclines to the right.

—   Shell length similar to height and less than 2x breadth; apex central (view from above) (fig. D2b)—
                Planorbidae - part: *Ancylus fluviatilis* **(river limpet)**

Up to 10 mm long. Common in lakes, ponds and streams; often in fast-flowing water.

a)   b)

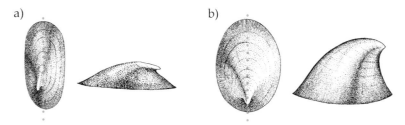

Fig. D2. Typical limpet shell forms of: (a) Acroloxidae; (b) Planorbidae: *Ancylus*. Dorsal views are shown on the left and lateral views on the right.

4(2) Operculum present (fig. D3)—   **5**

—   Operculum absent—   **9**

a)   b)

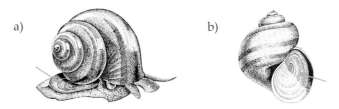

Fig. D3. Viviparidae: (a) with the operculum on its back arrowed; (b) with the operculum retracted to seal the shell aperture arrowed.

5   Shell aperture semi-circular (fig. D4a)—   **Neritidae**

Height up to 6 mm; breadth up to 11 mm. 1 species: *Theodoxus fluviatilis.*
Common on stones in larger calcareous rivers and streams. Tolerates brackish
water.

—   Shell aperture round or oval (fig. D4b,c,d)—   **6**

6   Shell height over 25 mm; usually banded (operculum with concentric
     rings) (fig. D3)—   **Viviparidae**

Height more than 30 mm. 1 genus: *Viviparus*; 2 species. Mainly standing or slow-
flowing deep waters.

—   Shell height less than 17 mm; rarely banded (operculum with concentric
     rings or with a spiral)—   **7**

7   Shell height and breadth about equal (fig. D4b) OR shell flat and disc-
     like (confirm operculum is present) OR shell about twice as broad as
     high; aperture round; operculum with a spiral—   **Valvatidae**

1 genus: *Valvata*; 3 species. Associated with mud in ponds, lakes and ditches or
silty river margins.

—   Shell higher than broad (fig. D4c,d); aperture round or oval—   **8**

8   Operculum flush with shell aperture and with concentric rings—
Bithyniidae (fig. D4c)

1 genus: *Bithynia*; 2 species. Standing and running calcareous waters.

—   Operculum recessed within the shell aperture, with a spiral line—
Hydrobiidae (spire shells) (fig. D4d)

Height less than 15 mm. 6 native genera: 6 native species. Also 1 introduced species: *Potamopyrgus antipodarum* (formerly known as *P. jenkinsi*). Ponds and streams; often occur as pioneer species in new water bodies in large numbers; dominant in brackish environments.

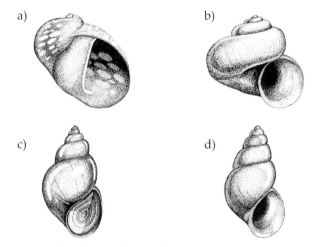

Fig. D4. Examples of operculate snails (with the operculum illustrated in c):
(a) Neritidae; (b) Valvatidae; (c) Bithyniidae; (d) Hydrobiidae.

9(4) Shell flattened (coiled in one plane) (fig. D5a)—
                    Planorbidae – part (ramshorn snails)

Height up to 12 mm; breadth up to 25 mm. 8 native genera; 15 native species
(including *Ancylus fluviatilis*; see couplet 3). Also 2 introduced genera and
species (*Ferrissia clessiniana*, formerly known as *F. wautieri*, and *Menetus
dilatatus*). Found in standing and slow-flowing waters of all sizes.

— Shell coiled and taller than broad (fig. D5b,c)—   **10**

10 Shell spire sinistral (fig. D5b) (if shell is held upright with the aperture
    towards the observer, the aperture is to the observer's left); shell
    glossy—   **Physidae (bladder snails)**

Height up to 17 mm. 2 native genera; 2 species; *Physa fontinalis* and *Aplexa
hypnorum*. Also 1 introduced genus (*Physella*, formerly included as part of *Physa*)
with 2 species (including *P. acuta*). Heavily vegetated water bodies including
rivers.

— Shell spire dextral (fig. D5c) (if shell is held upright with the aperture
    towards the observer, the aperture is to the observer's right); shell
    dull—   **Lymnaeidae (pond snails)**

Height up to 50 mm. 6 genera; 9 species. Found in standing and slow-flowing
waters of all sizes. Includes the common *Radix balthica*, which until recently was
known as *Lymnaea peregra*.

a) 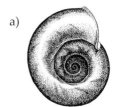 b) 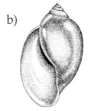 c)

Fig. D5. (a) Planorbidae with flattened shell; (b) Physidae with sinistral spire
shell; (c) Lymnaeidae with dextral spire shell.

Note: This next 'couplet' has three end points

11(1)Shell outline mytiliform (resembles a common marine mussel); hinge at anterior end reduced and pointed; posterior end expanded (fig. D6a); attached to the substratum by threads— **Dreisseniidae**

Length up to 40 mm; height up to 11 mm. Introduced, with 2 genera; 2 species. *Dreissena polymorpha* (zebra mussel), a Ponto-Caspian invader whose shell is generally distinctively striped, occurs in still or slow-flowing fresh water; *Mytilopsis leucophaeata* (dark false mussel), originally from the Gulf of Mexico, lives in brackish water. The two species could only be confused where their ranges overlap in lower river stretches.

The quagga mussel (*Dreissena rostriformis*, usually referred to by its subspecies name *D. r. bugensis*) is a Ponto-Caspian invader that is likely to turn up in Britain in the future. This species is distinguishable from *D. polymorpha* by looking at the seam between the two valves (fig. D7): in *D. polymorpha* the seam is straight (fig. D7a), whereas in *D. r. bugensis* it is wavy (fig. D7b).

— Shell outline ovoid (length only slightly greater than height) (fig. D6b); not attached to the substratum— **12**

— Shell elliptical (length much greater than the height) and at least 25 mm long, usually more (fig. D6c,d); edges of the mantle separate; not attached to the substratum— **Superfamily UNIONOIDEA**

Up to 180 mm long. 2 families. Margaritiferidae has one species: *Margaritifera margaritifera* (fig. D6c) (freshwater pearl mussel), which is the only large freshwater mussel found in rapidly flowing soft waters; it has a robust shell, which is usually eroded at the hinge. It is restricted to a few rivers in the north and west, being most widespread in Scotland and Ireland. Unionidae (fig. D6d) has three genera: *Unio* (2 spp.), *Anodonta* (swan mussels: 3 spp.) and *Pseudanodonta* (1 sp.); all three genera require calcium-rich hard water and are mainly found in the margins of rivers and canals where the sediment is muddy and compact.

12   Shell glossy and green in colour, with distinct concentric ridges—
Corbiculidae

Length up to 30 mm. One species: *Corbicula fluminea* (Asian clam), a south-east Asian invasive that was recorded in Britain for the first time in 1998 and in Ireland in 2010. Occurs in lakes, canals and slow-flowing rivers and can be extremely abundant.

—   Shell whitish or greyish, not glossy; concentric rings present but not as obvious ridges—   **Sphaeriidae (pea mussels)**

Up to 25 mm long, but many species considerably smaller. 3 genera; 22 species. Standing and slow-flowing waters, including wetlands; frequent in detritus and mud.

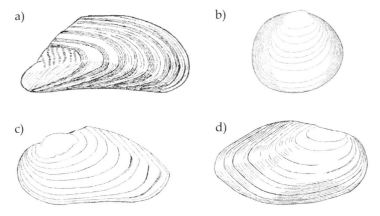

Fig. D6. Examples of Bivalvia shell shapes: (a) Dreisseniidae; (b) Sphaeriidae; (c) Margaritiferidae; (d) Unionidae.

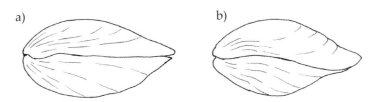

Fig. D7. Dreisseniidae. Lateral view of shell showing the seam between the valves: (a) *Dreissena polymorpha*; (b) *D. rostriformis bugensis*.

Key E – Crustacea

(Shrimps, crayfish, water fleas, copepods, ostracods and allies)

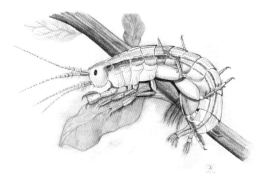

Gammarus pulex

Crustacea are extremely varied in morphology. They are characterised by having two pairs of jointed antennae, but in some species these are vestigial, in others they are hidden by an external carapace and in others they are adapted as feeding or even locomotory organs, so are difficult to identify as antennae. Within each group, however, there is normally a uniformity of structure so, if in doubt, compare initially with the illustrations to get an idea of what your animal might be.

The group that is likely to cause the most trouble for the beginner is the Ostracoda; these can easily be mistaken for plant seeds or bivalve molluscs, but look carefully for the jointed appendages protruding from the bivalve carapace and, if your specimen is alive, their ability to swim rapidly which instantly distinguishes them from molluscs.

Crustacea are the only group of animals in the guide that include large numbers of planktonic species, living suspended or swimming in the water column rather than on or under the bed of the water body. The class includes some of the smallest freshwater invertebrates as well as the largest. They are diverse in both fresh and salt water, and so the key includes a few essentially marine species that can stray into coastal fresh waters. Sometimes these are distinct families (e.g. Palaemonidae), but within the Gammaridae the genera *Gammarus* and *Echinogammarus* have fully marine as well as fully freshwater representatives.

Although not keyed out below it is worth mentioning the pre-adult stages. Many freshwater Crustacea, including Anostraca, Notostraca, Copepoda and Ostracoda, possess a free swimming larval (nauplius) stage in their development (fig. E11d). After hatching from the egg the nauplius has three pairs of functional appendages, a median eye and no external segmentation and therefore is morphologically very different from the adult. In contrast, larval development of other Crustacea, such as decapods and most cladocerans, occurs within the egg and when they hatch they resemble the adults in every way except size.

The Crustacean fauna is rapidly changing due to the arrival of invasive species native to the Ponto-Caspian region. Several Ponto-Caspian invaders have already colonised Britain and Ireland and at appropriate parts of the key we have mentioned others that may turn up in due course.

Notes on parasitic copepods

In addition to the three free-living orders of copepods (subclass Copepoda) keyed out below there are three orders of copepods (Poecilistomatoida, Cyclopoida and Siphonostomatoida) which parasitise British freshwater fish. With the exception of one species, only the adult females are parasitic.

The order Poecilistomatoida includes a single freshwater family, the Ergasilidae. This has a body similar in appearance to the Cyclopoida (see fig. E1) but its first antenna (antennule) consists of five (genus *Thersitina*) or six (genera *Ergasilus* and *Neoergasilus*) segments whereas the first antenna of Cyclopoida typically has more than six segments. The second antenna in Ergasilidae is prehensile, being adapted for grasping prey, and is far more prominent in females than in males (fig. E1). There are 3 genera and 5 species. All are less than 2 mm in length.

The order Cyclopoida is free-living with the exception of females of *Lernaea cyprinacea* (Lernaeidae) which parasitise freshwater fish. Both males and females have a characteristic body form which is unlike the other species of freshwater cyclopoid copepods (fig. E2). They are up to 10 mm long.

Two families in the order Siphonostomatoida – Caligidae and Lernaeopodidae – are represented in Britain's fresh waters. Caligidae has a single species – *Lepeophtheirus salmonis* – of which both the males and females parasitise fish; its body is more or less flattened (fig. E3) and it is able to move on its host. It is up to 20 mm long and often obvious on the bodies of salmon, the only fish it parasitises; however, as a marine species it does not normally persist in fresh waters for more than a few days. Lernaeopodidae are characterised by their two fused maxillary arms which they use to attach to their host (fig. E4). The males typically cling to the body of the female. There are 3 genera and 6 species, up to 10 mm long.

a)

b)

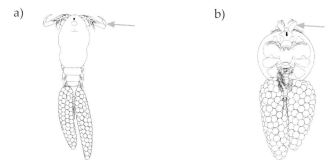

Fig. E1. Ergasilidae with second antenna arrowed: (a) *Ergasilus* sp., adult female, dorsal view; (b) *Thersitina* sp., adult female, ventral view.

Fig. E2. Lernaeidae: *Lernaea cyprinacea*. Arrow points to anchor which in life is embedded in the host.

Fig. E3. Caligidae: *Lepeophtheirus salmonis*, adult male, dorsal view.

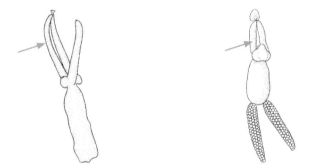

Fig. E4. Lernaeopodidae: examples of adult females, with maxillary arms arrowed.

Key to adult Crustacea

1 With at least 10 consecutive leaf-like limbs of similar appearance; when alive the animal is in constant motion – the undulations of its limbs, moving one after the other in a rhythmic sequence, drive it along—

Subclass BRANCHIOPODA – part: 2

— Fewer than 10 consecutive limbs of similar appearance— **3**

2 Without a carapace (a protective hard shield-like plate covering the head and thorax); a pair of black eyes on stalks (fig. E5)—

Order ANOSTRACA

Two species. *Chirocephalus diaphanus* (the fairy shrimp, family Chirocephalidae) is up to 35 mm long and found in temporary pools. In Britain, there are scattered records in England and Wales of which the most northerly is near York. *Tanymastix stagnalis* (family Tanymastigiidae), usually to 16 mm long, occurs in Ireland in temporary waters.

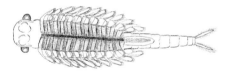

Fig. E5. Chirocephalidae: *Chirocephalus diaphanus*, ventral view.

— With a carapace; eyes not placed on the end of stalks (fig. E6)—

Order NOTOSTRACA

Up to 40 mm long. One species: *Triops cancriformis* (the tadpole shrimp, family Triopsidae), formerly known as *Apus cancriformis*. Found in temporary pools. Very rare in the British Isles.

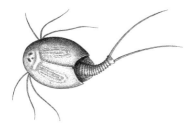

Fig. E6. Triopsidae: *Triops cancriformis*, dorsal view*

* The illustration used is that by the German natural historian Jacob Christian Schäffer (1718-1790), here repeated more than 250 years after it first appeared in 1756. Schäffer was the first to observe the hatching of a resting egg and the emerging nauplius larva of *Triops*. His work on these animals has been largely forgotten, but the survival and continual use of his outstanding illustrations is a fitting tribute to this extraordinary man.

3(1) Shrimp-like, woodlouse-like, crayfish-like or crab-like in appearance, and usually longer than 5 mm (exception is *Antrobathynella stammeri*; c.1 mm and with a very distinct appearance [fig. E12]) with many appendages: four pairs of legs to the thorax, the first one or three pairs often modified as mouthparts; three pairs of appendages to the abdomen, the last sometimes modified to form part of a tail fan—
Subclass MALACOSTRACA: 15

— Adults usually less than 3 mm long with five or fewer pairs of appendages— **4**

4 Body enclosed within a bivalve carapace with a distinct hinge dorsally; can have the appearance of a plant seed as all the limbs can be withdrawn within the carapace (fig. E7)—
Subclass OSTRACODA (ostracods)

Up to 7 mm long, but usually less than 3 mm. 8 families; 26 genera; c. 90 species. All types of waters, usually associated with vegetation or substratum.

Fig. E7. Ostracoda, lateral view.

— Bivalve carapace absent or, if present, without a dorsal hinge and does not enclose the head— **5**

5   Second antenna large and usually with two branches; the head
     projects from a trunk that is often enclosed by a bivalve carapace; body
     generally with no obvious traces of segmentation apart from a series of
     limbs; single median compound eye—
          Subclass BRANCHIOPODA – part (CLADOCERA) (water fleas): 6

It is generally agreed that 'cladocera' consists of four quite distinct orders and
that the term 'cladocera' now has no clearly defined taxonomic significance
but remains a useful descriptive term. Males are less common than females
and in some cases absent during a large part of the year, the females being
able to produce eggs and young parthenogenetically. At certain times of the
year, particularly in autumn or under adverse conditions such as threatened
drying up of temporary ponds, males make their appearance. Females are often
distinguishable by the presence of eggs or young in a dorsal brood sac. The key
below is for females only.

—   Second antenna small and unbranched; body cylindrical, obviously
     segmented and without carapace, or in the case of *Argulus*, with a flat
     shield-like carapace—   **12**

6   Animal embedded in a mass of jelly; second antennae with one branch
     (fig. E8a)—   **Order CTENOPODA: Holopedidae**

Up to 2.5 mm long. 1 species: *Holopedium gibberum*. Exclusively planktonic in
lakes with clear, soft water. Swims on its back, supported in the water by its
gelatinous mantle.

—   Animal not embedded in a mass of jelly; second antenna with two
     branches—   **7**

7   Trunk and limbs enclosed in a carapace (see fig. E8)—   **8**

—   Carapace not enclosing trunk and limbs, forming a brood-sac for
     eggs (see fig. E9)—   **10**

Note: This next 'couplet' has three end points
8   Second antenna long, with three segments in one branch and two
     segments in the other (fig. E8b)—   **Order CTENOPODA: Sididae**

Up to 4 mm long. 3 genera; 4 species. Vegetated edges of lakes or in plankton.

— Second antenna short, with three segments in each branch (fig. E8c)—
Order ANOMAPODA – part: Chydoridae

Up to 4 mm long. 19 genera; 42 species. Very diverse habits: often found among weeds or mud in ponds and lakes.

— Second antenna with four segments in one branch and three segments in the other—
Order ANOMAPODA - part: 9

Note: This next 'couplet' has FOUR end points
9   (NB. Caeca [singular: caecum] are small pouches of the gut; they are clearly visible as the animals are generally transparent)—

— First antenna large and movable, with sensilla (slender sensory organs) at the tip; caeca absent from the anterior end of the gut (except *Ophryoxus*, found in a few Scottish lochs) (fig. E8d)—   **Macrothricidae**

Up to 1 mm long. 8 genera; 11 species. Found in vegetated water bodies, usually near the bed.

— First antenna large with a small tuft of sensilla at its tip; head large relative to body size; two caeca at the anterior end of the gut (fig. E8e)—   **Moinidae**

Up to 2 mm long. One genus: *Moina*; 3 species. Small still water bodies.

— First antenna small and inconspicuous; two caeca at the anterior end of the gut (fig. E8f)—   **Daphniidae**

Up to 5 mm long. 3 genera; 22 species. From small still water bodies and shallow lake edges to the plankton of large lakes.

— First antenna large and immobile, with a small tuft of setae midway between the base and the tip (fig. E8g)—   **Bosminidae**

Up to 1 mm long. One genus: *Bosmina*; 3 species. Lakes and ponds.

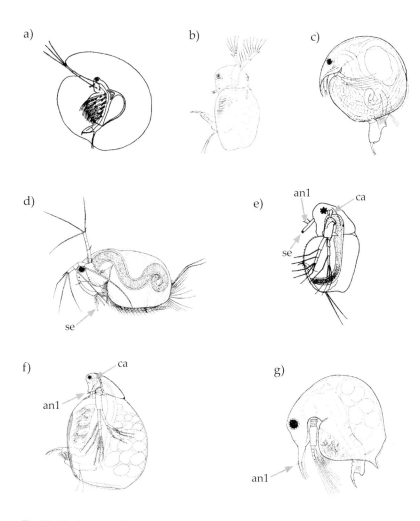

Fig E8. Cladocera orders Ctenopoda and Anomapoda, all in lateral view:
(a) Holopedidae; (b) Sididae; (c) Chydoridae; (d) Macrothricidae, showing
sensilla (*se*); (e) Moinidae, showing caeca, *ca*, sensilla, *se*, and 1st antenna, *an1*;
(f) Daphniidae, showing 1st antenna, *an1*, and caeca, *ca*; (g) Bosminidae,
showing 1st antennae, *an1*.

10(7)Six pairs of legs; body elongate (fig. E9a)— **Order HAPLOPODA**

> Up to 10 mm long. One species: *Leptodora kindti* (family Leptodoridae). Open water in lakes.

— Four pairs of legs; body compact (excluding caudal process)—
Order ONYCHOPODA: 11

11 Caudal process about as long as the head (fig. E9b)— **Polyphemidae**

> Up to 2 mm long. One species: *Polyphemus pediculus*. Vegetated margins of lakes.

— Caudal process very much longer than the body (fig. E9c)—
Cercopagidae

> Up to 3 mm long. One genus: *Bythotrephes*. 2 species. Open water in lakes.

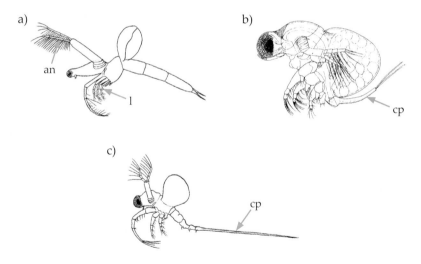

Fig. E9. Cladocera: orders Haplopoda and Onychopoda, all in lateral view.
(a) *Leptodora kindti*, Leptodoridae, showing legs, *l*, and antenna, *an*;
(b) *Polyphemus pediculus*, Polyphemidae, showing caudal process, *cp*;
(c) *Bythotrephes*, Cercopagidae, showing caudal process, *cp*.

12(5)With a flat shield-like carapace; two ventral suckers (fig. E10)—
Subclass Branchiura

Up to 13 mm long. One genus: *Argulus* (family Argulidae); 3 species. Fish lice, living attached to body or mouth of fish, but can leave host and swim freely.

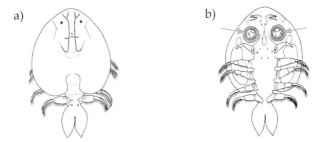

Fig. E10 Argulidae, *Argulus* sp: (a) dorsal view; (b) ventral view with suckers arrowed.

— Body cylindrical and segmented with no carapace and no suckers—
Subclass COPEPODA: 13

See note at the beginning of Key E (page 49) on parasitic copepods.

13   Cephalothorax (head and thorax combined into a single structure) about the same width as abdomen and not clearly separated from it; first antenna very short, never exceeding 10 segments (fig. E11a); non-swimming—   **Order HARPACTICOIDA**

Up to 1 mm long. 8 families; 16 genera; 43 species. Most habitats on surfaces and in sediments.

— Cephalothorax wider than abdomen and clearly separated from it (E11b, c); first antenna longer; free swimming—   **14**

14   First antenna with 22 to 25 segments (17 to 18 in the brackish-water
      genus *Acartia*); second antenna two-branched; egg-sac (if any) single
      (fig. E11b)—   **Order CALANOIDA**

      Up to 3 mm long. 4 families; 8 genera; 16 species. Still waters, often planktonic.
      Usually in open water.

—   First antenna with 6 to 17 segments; second antenna unbranched; egg-
      sacs paired (fig. E11c)—   **Order CYCLOPOIDA (excl. Lernaeidae)**

      Up to 3 mm long. 3 families; 19 genera; 46 species. In a wide range of water
      bodies. See note at the beginning of Key E (page 49) on parasitic copepods.

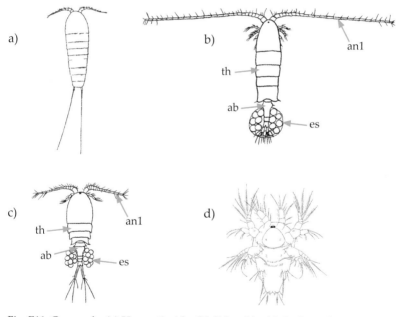

Fig. E11. Copepoda: (a) Harpacticoida; (b) Calanoida; (c) Cyclopoida;
(d) example of nauplius of Cyclopoida. Arrows point to egg sacs, *es*, 1st antenna,
an1, thorax, *th* and abdomen, *ab*.

15(3)Without a carapace, i.e. thoracic segments apparent when viewed from above; eyes (when present) not on stalks— **16**

— With a carapace; eyes on stalks— **27**

16 Very small, elongate, colourless body; thoracic legs two-branched, except the last (fig. E12)— **Order BATHYNELLACEA**

Up to 1 mm long. 1 species: *Antrobathynella stammeri* (family Bathynellidae). Ground waters, caves. Bathynellids belong to the Syncarida, a very ancient division of Crustacea. They are indeed malacostracans, like all the groups that follow in this key, despite their unusual appearance.

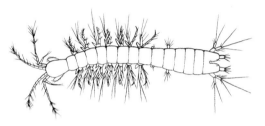

Fig. E12. Bathynellidae: *Antrobathynella stammeri*, dorsal view.

— Larger, with unbranched thoracic legs— **17**

17 Woodlouse-like, dorsally flattened (fig. E13b)— **Order ISOPODA: 18**

Up to 15 mm long. 1 family: Asellidae; 3 genera; 4 species, all formerly included in the genus *Asellus*. Found in still or slow flowing water with detritus, often in polluted environments.

The marine isopods *Lekanesphaera*, formerly known as *Sphaeroma* (Sphaeromatidae, fig. E13a) and *Jaera* (Janiridae) often occur in fresh water at the edge of salt marshes, but they are not truly freshwater species; both are more oval in general body shape than asellids. The freshwater Ponto-Caspian *Jaera istri*, which looks superficially similar to *Lekanesphaera* but can persist in inland waters, may appear in British waters soon.

— Shrimp-like, laterally flattened (e.g. fig. E16)— **Order AMPHIPODA (shrimps): 20**

18   Pigmented and with eyes—   **19**

—   Without pigment; eyes absent (fig. E13c)—   *Proasellus cavaticus*

Caves and ground waters.

19   Two pale head spots (fig. E13d)—   *Asellus aquaticus* **(hoglouse)**

By far the most common British aquatic isopod, found in a variety of fresh
waters but indicative particularly of detritus rich or organically polluted water.
Caecidotea communis, a species introduced from North America, will also key
out here; it has been recorded from a single location in the UK: Bolam Lake in
Northumberland.

—   One continuous white patch on head (this pattern may be obscured
by detritus, so use a needle to clean it off before making observations)
(fig. E13e)—   *Proasellus meridianus*

Distribution and habitat similar to *Asellus aquaticus*.

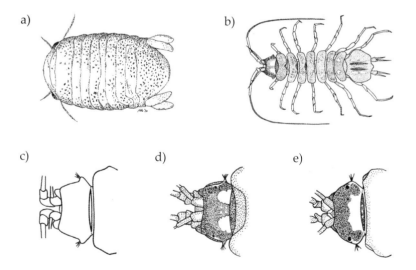

Fig. E13. Isopoda, all in dorsal view: (a) Sphaeromatidae: *Lekanesphaera* whole
animal; (b-e) Asellidae: (b) *Asellus aquaticus*, whole animal; (c-e) heads of
(c) *Proasellus cavaticus*, (d) *Asellus aquaticus*, (e) *Proasellus meridianus*.

20(17) Second antenna very large and robust, more than half as long as the
body; head and body not markedly flattened (fig. E14)— **Corophiidae**

Up to 9 mm long. 2 genera: *Chelicorophium*; 5 species. Most are transitional zone species, usually in brackish conditions. One truly freshwater species, *Chelicorophium curvispinum* (referred to in some guides as *Corophium curvispinum*), is colonising western Europe from its Ponto-Caspian origins, using the canal system as a means of dispersal. It was first recorded in Britain in 1935, is now widely distributed in the English Midlands, and since 2000 has been recorded from several loughs in Ireland.

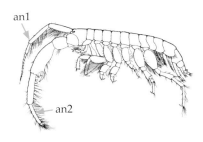

Fig. E14. Corophidae, lateral view: *Chelicorophium*, showing 1st, *an1*, and 2nd, *an2*, antennae.

— Second antenna less than half the length of the body; head and body
distinctly flattened from side to side— **21**

21 First antenna very short, less than a quarter of the whole length of the
second antenna (fig. E15)— **Talitridae**

Up to 20 mm long. 1 species: *Orchestia cavimana*. Semi-terrestrial, on edges of rivers or canals; plus marine environments. First recorded in Britain in 1942, it is believed to be southern European in origin. Its distribution is currently fairly localised, but it has recently expanded its range greatly in north-eastern Europe and so may become more widespread in Britain.

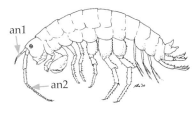

Fig. E15. Talitridae: *Orchestia cavimana*, lateral view, showing 1st, *an1*, and 2nd, *an2*, antennae.

— First and second antennae approximately the same length (fig. E16)
(in most cases first antenna is slightly longer)— **22**

22   Eyes absent— **23**

—   Eyes present— **24**

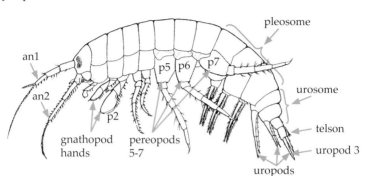

Fig. E16. Gammaridae: *Gammarus pulex*, lateral view, showing location of features used in identification of amphipods.

23   Gnathopod hands (see fig. E16) longer than broad (fig. E17a)—
Crangonyx subterraneus

Up to 6 mm long. One of two species in the family Crangonyctidae. Groundwater.

—   Gnathopod hands about as broad as long (fig. E17b)—   **Niphargidae**

Up to 15 mm long. 1 genus: *Niphargus* (fig. E17c); 5 species. Groundwater and sediments beneath surface waters.

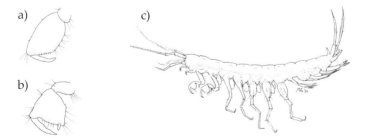

Fig. E17. Amphipoda: (a-b) gnathopod 2, (a) *Crangonyx subterraneus*; (b) *Niphargus* sp.; (c) *Niphargus aquilex*, whole animal, lateral view.

24(22) This couplet requires looking at the telson and uropod 3, the appendages at the posterior end of the abdomen (fig. E16). Uropod 3 consists of two pairs of extensions, of which the inner one is the endopod and the outer one is the exopod (fig. E19c-f)

— Rear abdominal segments generally smooth in appearance, or with short fine setae (fig. E18b). Telson with a V-shaped indentation, but otherwise clearly a single structure; exopod without setae, but with distinct spines (fig. E19c)— *Crangonyx pseudogracilis*

Up to 10 mm long. Further confirmation can be obtained by looking at pereopods 5-7 (see fig. E16), on which the posterior edge of the 2nd segment (basis) is strongly serrated and not armed with spines or prominent setae (fig. E19a). One of two species in the family Crangonyctidae. Introduced from North America, probably during the 1930s, and now widely distributed. When living, can look bluish in colour.

— Abdominal segments with dorsal setae, spines or projections (fig. E18c-f). Telson with a deep cleft dividing it into two distinct halves; exopod has distinct tufts of setae, normally also with some spines but these are not always obvious (fig. E19d-f)— **Gammaridae: 25**

As a further distinction from *Crangonyx*, on pereopods 5-7, the posterior edge of the 2nd segment is relatively smooth or slightly notched (fig. E19b).

25 Abdominal urosome segments 1 and 2 each with a dorsal projection (figs E18a,f; see also fig. E19e)— *Dikerogammarus*

Up to 30 mm long. Native to the Ponto-Caspian region but rapidly spreading in western Europe. *Dikerogammarus villosus* (often referred to as the killer shrimp) first appeared in Britain in 2010; it is more aggressive than native amphipods, predating on a range of invertebrates including other amphipods. *Dikerogammarus haemobaphes* was first recorded in Britain in 2012, and a third species - *D. bispinosus* - is likely to appear in due course. To separate the three species, look at the shape of the projections on the urosome and the number of spines at the tip. In *D. haemobaphes* the projections are shallow, typically with 2 large spines. Both *D. villosus* and *D. bispinosus* have pointed dorsal projections (as in fig. E18f), but *D. villosus* has 3-5 spines whereas *D. bispinosus* has 2. Some consider this genus to be in a separate family, Pontogammaridae.

— Urosome of abdomen without conical projections, although distinct tufts of setae or spines are normally present— **26**

26   Endopod less than one quarter length of exopod (fig. E19d)—

Echinogammarus

Up to 20 mm long. *Echinogammarus berilloni*, known from the Channel Islands, is distinctive in having the abdomen in mature adult males covered with numerous tufts of long curved setae sometimes with scattered small spines in between them (less obvious in adult females and juveniles) (fig. E18c,d)

Echinogammarus ischnus is an invasive species from the Ponto-Caspian region that has recently expanded its range across central and Western Europe. It has high salt tolerance and is likely to turn up in Britain in due course. It lacks the distinct tufts of setae found in *E. berilloni*.

There are also several marine species of *Echinogammarus* native to Britain and Ireland and found particularly in the intertidal zone.

—   Endopod more than one third length of exopod (fig. E19f)— *Gammarus*

Up to 25 mm long. 4 native species in fresh waters. Found in all types of still and slow-flowing water, including brackish (and some species are fully marine). The most widespread species in Britain is *Gammarus pulex* which, along with *G. lacustris*, is confined to fresh waters. In Ireland and the Isle of Man, where *G. pulex* is not native, it is replaced by *G. duebeni*, which is mainly confined to estuarine water elsewhere in its range. The estuarine species *G. zaddachi* occasionally occurs in rivers close to their mouths. A fifth species, *G. tigrinus*, was introduced from North America. *Gammarus pulex* was introduced to the Isle of Man in the 1940s and has more recently been introduced to rivers in Northern Ireland, where it is gradually replacing *G. duebeni* as the freshwater species.

There are also several fully marine species of *Gammarus* native to Britain and Ireland.

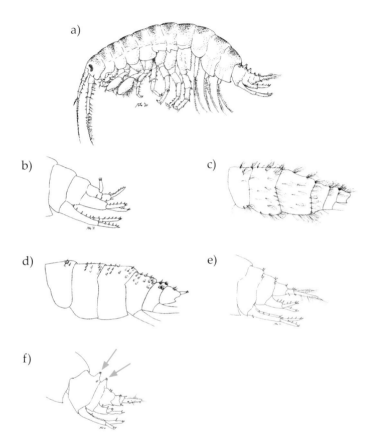

Fig. E18 Amphipoda. (a) *Dikerogammarus villosus*, whole animal, lateral view; (b-f) lateral view of posterior of abdomen: (b) *Crangonyx pseudogracilis*; (c -d) *Echinogammarus berilloni* (c) male, (d) female; (e) *Gammarus* sp.; (f) *D. villosus*, with arrows pointing to urosome projections.

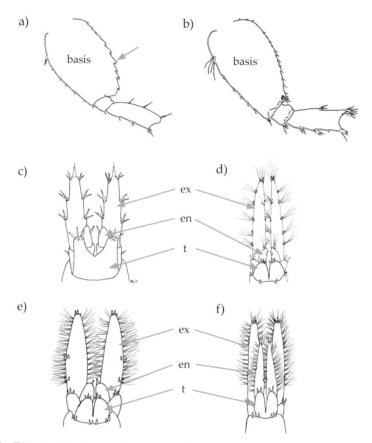

Fig. E19. Amphipoda. (a-b) upper part of a pereopod of (a) *Crangonyx pseudogracilis*, with arrow pointing to serrated edge; (b) *Gammarus* sp. (c-f) dorsal view of rear of abdomen of (c) *Crangonyx pseudogracilis*; (d) *Echinogammarus* sp.; (e) *Dikerogammarus* sp.; (f) *Gammarus* sp. Arrows point to the exopod, *ex*, endopod, *en* and telson, *t*.

Note: This next 'couplet' has three end points

27(15) Body crab-like with large pincers on the anterior limbs; thick mat of bristles on the claws (fig. E20) — *Eriocheir sinensis*

Up to 50 mm in carapace width. The Chinese mitten crab (family Grapsidae). Introduced from eastern Asia. Lives in fresh water, but must return to the sea to breed. It burrows into soft banks and has been found in the lower reaches of slow-flowing rivers in eastern England. Note: truly marine crabs may occasionally occur close to the mouths of rivers or the landward edge of salt marshes; they can be distinguished from *E. sinensis* by the absence of the claw bristles.

Fig. E20. Grapsidae: *Eriocheir sinensis*, dorsal view.

— Body lobster-like with large pincers on the anterior limbs (fig. E21a) — **28**

— Body not as above; no large pincers on anterior limbs (figs E22 E23a) — **31**

28 A large curved spine or spur present on the inside of the front carpus (penultimate leg segment) (fig. E21b) — **Cambaridae**

Up to 150 mm long. 2 genera; 2 species. *Procambarus clarkii* (red swamp crayfish) and *Orconectes limosus* were introduced from North America via mainland Europe, but are currently very localised in southern England, particularly London.

— No prominent large curved spine or spur on the inside of carpus (Note: strong spines may be seen on juveniles of *Austropotamobius pallipes*; in adults these become small projections on the carpus and in some specimens they remain as relatively short spines) — **Astacidae: 29**

29 Head with a single ridge on each side; sides of rostrum (the narrow extension at the front of the head) converge towards the front (fig. E21a, c) — *Austropotamobius pallipes* (**white-clawed crayfish**)

Up to 120 mm long. The native crayfish of Britain. Streams. Formerly throughout Britain (localised in Scotland) but now widely replaced by *Pacifastacus* and distribution localised. Widespread in Ireland.

— Head with two ridges on each side; sides of rostrum relatively parallel towards the front (fig. E21d, e) — **30**

30   Sides and median ridge of rostrum is clearly toothed (fig. E21d)—

Astacus

Up to 180 mm long. 2 species, including *A. leptodactylus*, the Turkish crayfish. Introduced from mainland Europe but currently very localised in southern England.

—   Sides and median ridge of rostrum smooth (fig. E21e)—

Pacifastacus leniusculus (signal crayfish)

Up to 160 mm long. Rivers and streams. Introduced from North America and now the dominant species throughout much of Britain. Currently absent from Ireland.

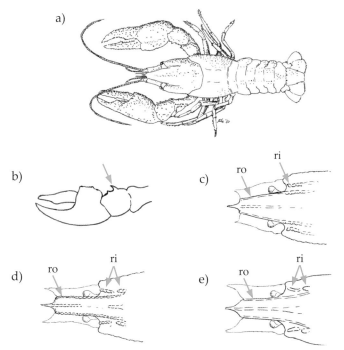

Fig. E21. Crayfish: (a) *Austropotamobius pallipes*, whole animal, dorsal view; (b) front limb of Cambaridae with the large spur on the carpus arrowed; (c-e) heads in dorsal view, with ridges, *ri* and rostrum, *ro* arrowed of (c) *Austropotamobius pallipes*; (d) *Astacus leptodactylus*; (e) *Pacifastacus leniusculatus*.

31(27) Thoracic limbs each with two branches —   **Mysidae: 32**

— Thoracic limbs each with a single branch (fig. E22) —   **Palaemonidae**

Up to 50 mm long. 2 genera; 2 species. These are marine and brackish water prawns that can live in fresh water so are occasionally encountered in coastal areas, but need to return to the sea to breed. Both are translucent when alive.

The freshwater prawn (*Atyaephyra desmarestii*; family Atyidae), will key out here. It is absent from Britain and Ireland but found in large rivers in adjacent parts of mainland Europe.

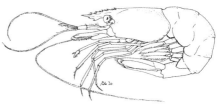

Fig. E22. Palaemonidae: *Palaemonetes varians*, lateral view.

Note: This next 'couplet' has three end points

32   Rear edge of telson (last abdominal division, fig. E23a) with a V-shaped cleft (fig. E23b) —   *Mysis salemaai* **(opossum shrimp)**

Up to 18 mm long. In Britain only in Ennerdale Water (Cumbria) where not seen for many years; more widespread in lakes and large rivers in Ireland. Formerly known as *M. relicta*. *Limnomysis benedeni* is a Ponto-Caspian species that is likely to appear in Britain in the near future. Its telson is cleft but is edged by large spines.

— Telson tapers to a point (fig. E23c) —   *Neomysis integer*

Up to 17 mm long. A brackish-water species that is able to survive long periods of isolation in fresh water.

— Telson truncate (fig. E23d) —
        Hemimysis anomala **(bloody-red shrimp)** (fig. E23a)

Up to 11 mm long. Found in both brackish and fresh waters. Native to the Ponto-Caspian region, it was first recorded in Britain in 2004 and Ireland in 2008 and is now rapidly expanding in the English Midlands. Often with distinctive red pigmentation, hence its common name.

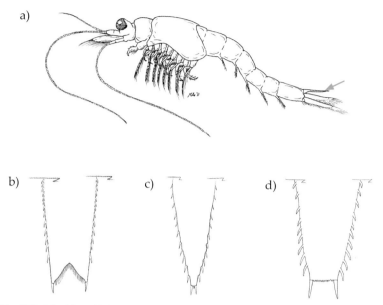

Fig. E23. Mysidae: (a) *Hemimysis anomala*, whole animal, lateral view, showing location of telson (arrow); (b-d) dorsal view of telson of: (b) *M. salemaai*, dorsal view of telson; (c) *Neomysis integer*, dorsal view of telson; (d) *Hemimysis anomala*, dorsal view of telson.

Key F – Insects

Coleoptera: Dytiscidae

Most aquatic insects are freshwater inhabitants only in the larval stage, the adults being terrestrial. The main exceptions are bugs (Hemiptera), in which all stages are aquatic, and beetles (Coleoptera), in which most species are aquatic as larvae and adults, although a few families are aquatic only as larvae or only as adults. The pupal stage of most beetles is terrestrial.

Insect larvae come in two fundamental types. Hemimetabolous insects (also known as Exopterygota) are those which lack a pupal stage; the juvenile form gradually develops adult characteristics as it grows. Holometabolous insects (also known as Endopterygota) have a larval stage that is morphologically very different to the adult, and undergo a complete metamorphosis during the pupal phase, in which the animal is normally inactive.

The juvenile stage of Exopterygota (Plecoptera, Ephemeroptera, Hemiptera, Odonata and Collembola) is often referred to as a nymph, the term 'larva', being confined to Endopterygota (Trichoptera, Coleoptera, Megaloptera, Hymenoptera and Diptera). However, most modern texts simply use the term 'larva' (plural: larvae) for all insect juvenile stages, a convention that we have adopted here.

Almost all aquatic insects, whether hemimetabolous or holometabolous, have three pairs of jointed legs and one pair of antennae, clearly identifying them as insects. The exceptions are larvae of a single, rarely encountered family of Coleoptera, the Curculionidae (weevils), and the largest order

72

of aquatic insects, the Diptera, or true flies. The Curculionidae and many Diptera have a distinct, hard head capsule and so are identifiable as arthropods, but quite a few Diptera either have a head capsule that is retractable into the thorax, and can therefore be easily overlooked, or is vestigial, with only internal hardened parts. If you are not sure whether your animal is a dipteran (Key M) or a true worm (Annelida: Key C), first compare with the illustrations.

All insects have a body divided into a head, a thorax and an abdomen. The thorax comprises three segments and it is on these that the legs will be situated, along with wings or wing buds, if present. Gills may be present on the thorax or the abdomen, occasionally both. The posterior end of the abdomen often supports appendages that are useful in identification; where these are long and slender, the term 'tail' is often used, as this describes their appearance very effectively.

Most insect groups are distinctive in morphology. The exception is the beetles: adult beetles are unmistakeable, but larvae come in a wide variety of forms, many with features - such as tails, abdominal hooks and gills – that overlap in form with those of other groups. Therefore beetle larvae appear at various different end points in the key below. If you are unsure of your diagnosis, comparing your specimen with the illustrations in subsequent keys should help.

The Key

1   Jointed legs present—   2

—   Jointed legs absent, although there may be prolegs—
                    Orders DIPTERA (true flies) and COLEOPTERA – part
                    (Curculionidae larvae): Key M (p148)

2   Underside of head with an extendable mask (fig. F1); body slender, with three leaf-like appendages at the end of the abdomen, or stout with small triangular appendages at the end of the abdomen—
                    Order ODONATA (dragonflies and damselflies): Key I (p99)

—   No mask on underside of head; if three long appendages at rear of abdomen, they are slender and not flattened—   3

Fig. F1. Odonata, Anisoptera: (a) whole animal in ventral view with mask arrowed; (b) lateral view of head with mask partially extended.

3   Two or three long slender tails at the end of the abdomen AND wing buds (fig. F2)—   4

Note: wing buds may only be obvious in more mature specimens.

—   Tails absent, a single tail or, if more than one tail present, there are no wing buds—   5

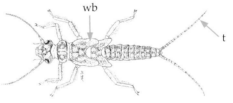

Fig. F2. Plecoptera. Dorsal view showing wing buds, *wb*, and posterior tails, *t*.

4   Plate-like or feathery gills present on up to seven abdominal segments (in the family Caenidae all gills except first pair are hidden beneath a large pair of gill covers); a single claw at the end of each leg; normally three long slender tails at the end of the abdomen—
                    Order EPHEMEROPTERA (mayflies): Key G (p80)

All British species of mayflies have three tails, but in other parts of the world there are some species with a very short central tail, giving the impression of only two tails; these include *Acentrella* (Baetidae) and *Epeorus* (Heptageniidae), found in mainland western Europe.

—   Gills absent or confined to thorax or rear end of the abdomen; two claws at the end of each leg; two long slender tails at the end of the abdomen—   **Order PLECOPTERA (stoneflies): Key H (p90)**

Note: This next 'couplet' has three end points.

5(3) A short-bodied animal with a single forked appendage present, folded
beneath the rear of the abdomen (may be extended behind the abdomen
in dead specimens); no other appendages on the abdomen (fig. F3)—
Class ENTOGNATHA, sub-class COLLEMBOLA (springtails)

Generally less than 5 mm long. 13 genera; 22 species. Found mainly in soil and
litter, a few in fresh waters and several are found in the marine littoral; rare in
dry conditions. *Podura aquatica* is common and lives on the water surface.

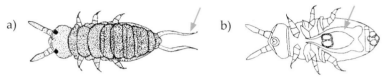

Fig. F3. Collembola, with arrows highlighting the forked appendage: (a) dorsal
view showing the forked appendage extended; (b) ventral view, showing the
forked appendage in its normal position folded beneath its abdomen.

— A single long tail-like rear extension is present, never folded or
forked—   6

Note: this endpoint includes the hemipteran family Nepidae, which has two
long appendages at the rear of the body, usually held together to form a single
tube (fig. F5b).

— Normally no slender extensions at end of the abdomen (although there
may be hooks or short appendages); if long tails present, the animal
looks more like those in fig. 4 than that in fig. 2.—   7

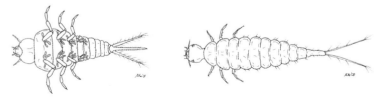

Fig. F4. Examples of Coleoptera larvae with tails. See Key L (page 137) for
further identification .

Note: This next 'couplet' has three end points

6   Jointed appendages, superficially leg-like, present along each side of the
     abdomen; large pincer-like jaws; wings absent (fig. F5a)—
                              Order MEGALOPTERA (alderflies): Sialidae

Up to 25 mm long. 1 genus (*Sialis*); 3 species. Larvae with jointed filamentous
gills covered in fine setae and body ending in a single long appendage. Typically
in mud at the bottom of ponds, lakes and streams.

—   No appendages along each side of the abdomen; jaws fused into a
     piercing organ; wings may be present (fig. F5b)—
                         Order HEMIPTERA (true bugs) - part: Key J (p105)

a)   b)

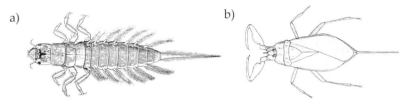

Fig. F5. (a) Sialidae; (b) Hemiptera (Nepidae), both in dorsal view.

—   Abdominal appendages absent or, if present, not jointed; jaws adapted
     for biting, with paired mandibles; wings absent—
                  Order COLEOPTERA (beetle larvae) - part: Key L (p137)

Note: This next 'couplet' has three end points.

7(5) One pair of hooks at the end of the abdomen, widely separated and
      often on the end of a long prolegs; abdomen fleshy; gills either feathery
      tufts, filaments laying flat against the body or absent; may be in a fixed
      net, fixed stone case or transportable case of stones or vegetation—
                         Order TRICHOPTERA (caddisflies): Key K (p113)

—   Two pairs of hooks, close together in the centre of the rear of the
     abdomen; gills long single filaments protruding from the abdomen—
                  Order COLEOPTERA (beetle larvae) - part: Key L (p137)

—   No hooks at end of the abdomen—   **8**

Note: This next 'couplet' has FOUR end points

8   Wings absent—   **9**

—   Wings present, enclosed in symmetrical hardened cases that cover most or all of the abdomen—
> **Order COLEOPTERA (beetle adults): Key L (p137)**

—   Wings present, without hardened cases and one overlapping the other—   **Order HEMIPTERA (true bugs) – part: Key J (p105)**

—   Wings present, without hardened cases and not overlapping (fig. F6)—
> Either **HYMENOPTERA (wasps),**
> OR **other terrestrial insect**

Hymenoptera: up to 10 mm long; more commonly c.1 mm. Parasitoid wasps, whose larvae live within the prey species and consume it from inside. 40 species in 11 families have been recorded from aquatic or semi-aquatic hosts, although few actively seek their hosts under water.

Agriotypus armatus (Ichneumonidae) attacks caddisfly larvae of the family Goeridae. The adult female (fig. F6a), up to 10 mm long, can spend several hours under water seeking host eggs. The larva develops when the caddisfly pupates, producing a distinctive narrow breathing tube that projects from the pupal case (fig. F6b). The larva (fig. F6c) is never free-living but if encountered outside its case would be difficult to distinguish from some Diptera larvae.

Very small wasps (fairy flies) of various families develop within the eggs of Odonata, Coleoptera, Diptera and Hemiptera. Up to 1 mm long, some can remain under water as adults for several days and *Caraphractus cinctus* (Mymaridae; formerly known as *Polynema natans*) (fig. F6d) can swim using wings adapted for underwater movement by the presence of long bristles.

Any other terrestrial insect may turn up in water, if it has fallen in. If still alive, it is most likely to be trapped in the surface film and clearly unable to swim, although some aquatic species will also struggle if caught in the surface film.

a)

b)

c)

d)

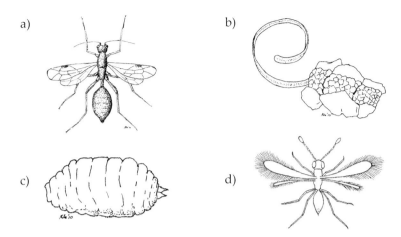

Fig. F6. Hymenoptera. (a-c) *Agriotypus armatus*: (a) adult female, dorsal view; (b) case of parasitised goerid caddisfly pupa, showing the distinctive breathing tube; (c) larva removed from case. (d) *Caraphractus cinctus*.

9   Five pairs of prolegs on the abdomen (on abdominal segments 3, 4, 5, 6 and 10); jointed legs small and stumpy; may be in a case made from pieces of vegetation (fig. F7)—
Order LEPIDOPTERA: Crambidae (china mark moths)

Up to 30 mm long. 5 genera; 5 species. Still and slowly flowing waters amongst vegetation; adults terrestrial. Included in the family Pyralidae in older texts. Look for a case made of aquatic plant parts to help confirm you have an aquatic species; when aquatic Lepidoptera are free from their cases they can be very difficult to distinguish from terrestrial species. Aquatic species never have long setae or brightly coloured bands on the abdomen or thorax, unlike many (but not all) terrestrial species.

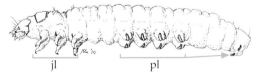

Fig. F7. Crambidae, lateral view showing jointed limbs, *jl* and prolegs, *pl*.

—   Prolegs absent—   **10**

Note: This next 'couplet' has three end points

10   Mouthparts comprise a pair of long slender tubes clearly extending beyond the front of the head (fig. F8)—   **Order NEUROPTERA**

Up to 20 mm long. 2 genera. There are 3 species of *Sisyra* (sponge flies: Sisyridae) which live in and feed on freshwater sponges. *Osmylus fulvicephalus* (a lacewing, family Osmylidae) lives in moss at the edge of streams.

a)

b)

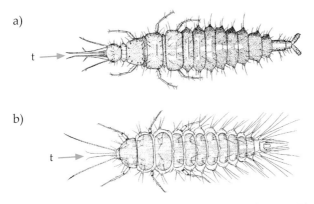

Fig. F8. Neuroptera: (a) *Osmylus*; (b) *Sisyra*, both in dorsal view with tubes, *t* arrowed.

—   Mouthparts fused into a downward pointing piercing structure, not extending beyond the front of the head—
         Order HEMIPTERA (true bugs) - part: Key J (p105)

—   Mouthparts comprise biting jaws, with paired mandibles—
         Order COLEOPTERA (beetle larvae) - part: Key L (p137)

Key G – Ephemeroptera

(Mayflies)

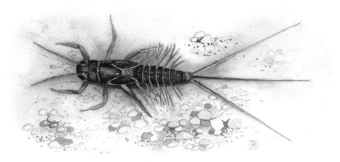

Paraleptophlebia

Mayfly larvae have up to seven pairs of gills attached to the sides of the abdominal segments. The number, shape and position of the gills are the main features used to separate most genera. Unfortunately, they are easily detached from the body, but rarely does a specimen lose all of its gills, so look closely for any that remain. Pick up specimens by the legs to prevent damage to the gills.

The Key

1   Gills under rounded covers (except small 1st pair of gills) – do not confuse gill covers (on abdomen) with wing buds (on thorax) (fig. G1)—

                                                                     Caenidae

    Up to 8 mm long. 2 genera; 9 species. Running and standing water (including temporary water bodies); mainly in mud and silt.

—   Gills visible on abdomen—   **2**

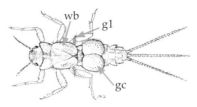

Fig. G1. Caenid larva with 1st gill, *g1*, gill covers, *gc* and wing buds, *wb* arrowed.

2   Gills feathery, each with two branches fringed with filaments (fig. G2a)—   **3**

—   Gills not feathery (fig. G2b-k), although they may have a small tuft of filaments at the base (fig. G2b)—   **4**

3   Gills held over back (fig. G3a); head with a pair of slender curved appendages (mandibles)—   **Ephemeridae**

Up to 25 mm long. 1 genus (*Ephemera*); 3 species. Running and standing waters; burrow in sand and gravel.

The family Polymitarcidae will also key out here. One species, *Ephoron virgo*, is widespread in larger rivers in mainland Europe but absent from Britain and Ireland. The two genera are distinguishable by the shape of the mandibles that project from the front of the heads: in *Ephemera* they are smooth and their tips diverge; in *Ephoron* they are spiny and their tips converge.

—   Gills held out sideways (fig. G3b); head without forward-pointing appendages—   **Potamanthidae**

Up to 15 mm long. 1 species: *Potamanthus luteus*. Running waters; usually large rivers. Localised, with recent records only from the Rivers Wye and Usk and adjacent areas.

4(2)   Body flattened; eyes on top of head (fig. G4); seven pairs of plate-like gills, each usually with a tuft of filaments attached at the base (fig. G2b)—   **5**

—   Body not flattened; eyes on side of head; gills slender or, if plate-like, without tufts of filaments (fig. G2c-k)—   **8**

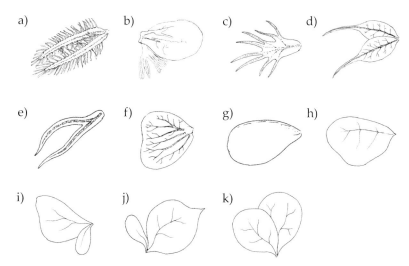

Fig. G2. Examples of mayfly gill shapes: (a) Ephemeridae; (b) Heptageniidae; (c-e) Leptophlebiidae: (c) *Habrophlebia*; (d) *Leptophlebia*; (e) *Paraleptophlebia* ; (f) Siphlonuridae; (g-k) Baetidae: (g) *Baetis*; (h) *Procloeon bifidum*; (i) *Procloeon pennulatum*; (j) *Cloeon simile*; (k) *Cloeon dipterum*.

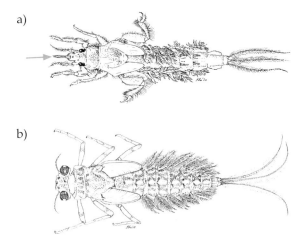

Fig. G3. (a) Ephemeridae, with arrow pointing to mandibles; (b) Potamanthidae. Both in dorsal view.

5   Long brush-like maxillary palps extend well beyond edges of the head
     and are conspicuous in both dorsal and ventral view (fig. G4b); each gill
     is a flat plate without a separate tuft of filaments— **Arthropleidae**

   Up to 14 mm long. 1 species: *Arthroplea congener*. This species probably does not
   occur in the British Isles, as there is only one record, from London in 1920.

—   Maxillary palps not as above and are shorter than the head; tufts of
     filaments are present on some or all of the plate-like gills (fig. G2b)—
                                                     Heptageniidae (fig. G4a): **6**

   Up to 18 mm long. 4 genera. Stony streams and rivers and on the stony shores of
   lakes.

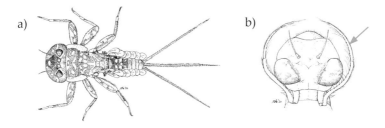

Fig. G4. (a) Heptageniidae: *Ecdyonurus*, whole animal, dorsal view;
(b) Athropleidae: *Arthroplea congener*: dorsal view of head with brush-like
maxillary palp arrowed.

6   Pronotum (plate covering first segment of thorax) has a backward
     projection on each side (fig. G5a)—   *Ecdyonurus* (3 species)

—   Pronotum without backward projections (fig. G5b)—   **7**

Fig. G5. Heptageniidae, dorsal view of head, pronotum and wing buds:
(a) backward projections on pronotum present (arrowed); (b) backward
projections on pronotum absent (arrowed).

7 First pair of gills considerably larger than others (fig. G6a); dorsal side of each femur with a dark dot in the centre— ***Rhithrogena*** (2 species)

— First gill small and like the others in shape (fig. G6b); femur without a dark dot in the centre—
     Heptagenia (3 species) and ***Electrogena*** (2 species)

Some recent publications have transferred *Heptagenia fuscogrisea* to a new genus, *Kageronia*, but this change is not widely accepted. The two species of *Electrogena* – *E. affinis* and *E. lateralis* – were formerly included in *Heptagenia*.

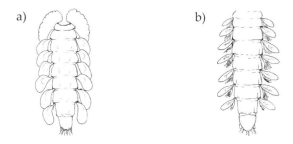

Fig. G6. Ventral view of abdomen of: (a) *Rhithrogena*; (b) *Heptagenia*.

8(4) Four pairs of plate-like gills which are held over back—
              Ephemerellidae (fig. G7): **9**

Up to 12 mm long. 2 genera. Fast-flowing streams and rivers.

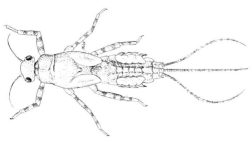

Fig. G7. Ephemerellidae, dorsal view.

— Six or seven pairs of gills visible from above and held out sideways— **10**

9   Abdominal segments with blunt spines on the dorsal surface, one on
     each side of the mid-line (fig. G8a); alternate light and dark bands on
     the tails—   *Serratella ignita*

—   Abdominal segments without blunt spines (fig. G8b); tails uniformly
     pigmented—   *Ephemerella notata*

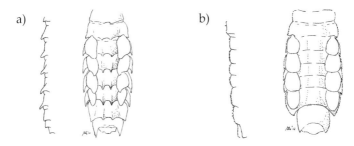

Fig. G8. Lateral profile and dorsal view of the abdominal tergites of: (a) *Serratella ignita*; (b) *Ephemerella notata*.

10(8) Gills composed of two or more long filaments (fig. G2c-e); tails equal to
      or greater than length of body—   **Leptophlebiidae** (fig. G9): **11**

      Up to 14 mm long. 3 genera.

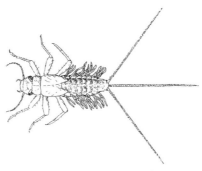

Fig. G9. Leptophlebiidae: *Paraleptophlebia*, dorsal view.

—   Gills plate-like and rounded (fig. G2f-k); tails shorter than length of
     body—   **13**

11   All seven pairs of gills are similar in shape and each gill has several
     branches (fig. G2c)—   *Habrophlebia fusca*

     Slow-flowing streams with aquatic macrophytes or dead leaves, sometimes
     rivers.

—   Each gill has only two branches—   **12**

12   Both branches of first gill are strap-shaped; the remaining six pairs of
     gills comprise two plates, each tapering to a single filament (fig. G2d)—
                                                      Leptophlebia

     2 species. Ponds, lakes and slow-flowing streams.

—   Both branches of all seven pairs of gills are strap-shaped (fig. G2e)—
                                                 Paraleptophlebia

     3 species. Streams and rivers.

13(10) Hind corners of posterior abdominal segments form sharp points
     (fig. G10a, b)—   **14**

—   Hind corners of posterior abdominal segments blunt (fig. G10c)—
                                             Baetidae (fig. G13): **15**

     Up to 12 mm long. 5 genera.

14   Spines on abdominal segments are small (fig. G10a); tails held close
     together in live larva; maxillae with comb-like bristles (fig. G11); seven
     pairs of gills, each gill single and oval—   **Ameletidae**

     Up to 11 mm long. 1 species: *Ameletus inopinatus*. Mountain streams.

—   Spines on abdominal segments are large and distinct (fig. G10b); tails
     held apart in live larvae; maxillae without comb-like bristles; seven
     pairs of gills, some with double plates which are mostly not oval
     (fig. G2f)—   **Siphlonuridae** (fig. G12)

     Up to 18mm. 1 genus: *Siphlonurus*; 3 species. Lakes and slow-flowing streams.

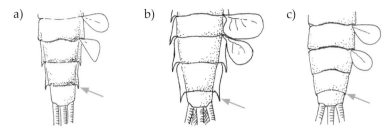

Fig. G10. Dorsal view of posterior abdominal segments with hind corners arrowed: (a) Ameletidae; (b) Siphlonuridae; (c) Baetidae. Gills are shown on the right hand side only.

Fig. G11. Mouthparts of *Ameletus inopinatus* with comb-like bristles on maxilla arrowed.

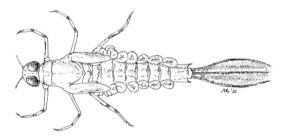

Fig. G12. Siphlonuridae: *Siphlonurus*, dorsal view.

15(13) All gills consist of single plates (fig. G2g, h)—   **16**

—   Six of the seven pairs of gills are double plates (fig. G2i-k)—   **17**

Note: This next 'couplet' has three end points

16   Middle tail is shorter than the outer ones (fig. G13a); tails never have dark rings but have a median dark band in some species—   *Baetis*

9 species. Streams and rivers. Several species in this genus have been transferred to new genera (*Alainites*, *Labiobaetis* and *Nigrobaetis*) in some recent publications, but these name changes are not widely accepted.

—   All three tails are the same length and have dark rings and a dark band (as in fig. G13c); each single gill is markedly asymmetrical—   *Procloeon bifidum*

Slow-flowing sections of streams and rivers.

—   All tails are the same length and but no wide dark band; each oval gill with a pointed tip—   *Centroptilum luteolum*

Stony shores of lakes and in slow-flowing sections of streams and rivers.

17(15) About five dark rings on each tail between the tip of the abdomen and the dark band (fig. G13c); tails held close together in live larvae—   *Procloeon pennulatum*

Can be further distinguished from *Cloeon* species by having gills that consist of one plate considerably larger than the other (as in *Cloeon simile*), but with a rounded tip to the larger plate (fig. G2i). Slow-flowing sections of streams and rivers, especially amongst vegetation.

—   More than five dark rings on each tail between the tip of the abdomen and the median dark band (fig. G13b); tails held well apart in live larvae and their tips curve downwards when viewed from the side (fig. G13b)—   *Cloeon*

2 species. *Cloeon simile* has gills with one plate considerably larger than the other, being distinguishable from those of *Procloeon pennulatum* by the larger plate having a pointed tip (fig. G2j); *Cloeon dipterum* has gills consisting of plates approximately equal in size (fig. G2k). Small ponds and slow-flowing sections of streams and rivers.

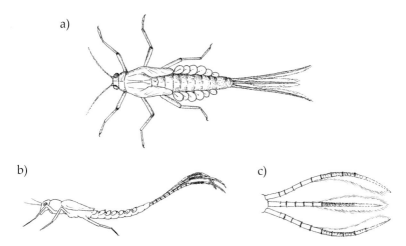

Fig. G13. Baetidae. (a) *Baetis*: whole animal, dorsal view; (b) *Cloeon simile* in life, lateral view, showing tails held at an angle to the body; (c) *Procloeon pennulatum* tails.

Key H – Plecoptera

(Stoneflies)

Isoperla grammatica

At first sight, identification of stoneflies can appear daunting, but it is fairly straightforward once a few morphological terms have been mastered. The key features to be looking for are in the mouthparts and on the abdomen.

In the mouthparts, which are situated on the ventral side of the head, you may be required to examine the submentum, the glossae and paraglossae, or the maxillary palps, all of which are highlighted in fig. H1.

The abdomen may be clearly divisible in at least some segments into an upper (tergum) and lower (sternum) section, with a line of demarcation along the side of the abdomen, as in figs H9 and H13. At the posterior end of the abdomen, the paraprocts are the paired triangular structures on the underside, as shown in figs H9 and H14.

Two methods can be used as the first step to separate stonefly families. The first involves looking at the relative length of the glossae and paraglossae (fig. H1). This is achieved by putting the specimen on its back and pushing the head down (no dissection necessary); it is important to push the head flat because if it is at an angle it is hard to determine relative length. Glossae are long (fig. H1a) in Taeniopterygidae, Nemouridae, Leuctridae and Capniidae, and short (fig. H1b) in Chloroperlidae, Perlidae and Perlodidae.

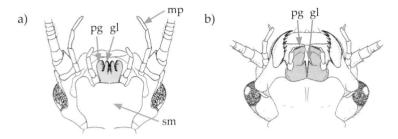

Fig. H1. Ventral view of heads of: (a) Leuctridae and (b) Chloroperlidae highlighting glossa, *gl* and paraglossa, *pg*. In (a) the glossae and paraglossae are equal in length, whereas in (b) the glossae are very short compared to the paraglossae. The submentum, *sm*, and maxillary palp, *mp*, are also highlighted in (a).

The second method is to look at the relative lengths of the three tarsal segments of the hind leg (fig. H2). This is best achieved by removing a hind leg and placing it on a slide with a cover slip to ensure the tarsus is lying flat.

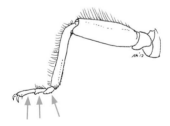

Fig. H2. Hind leg of Taeniopterygidae, highlighting the three tarsal segments.

The Key

Note: This 'couplet' has three end points

1   Tarsus of hind leg: all three segments similar in length (segment 3 may be slightly longer than the others) (fig. H3a); glossae as long as paraglossae (fig. H1a)—   Taeniopterygidae (fig. H4): **2**

—   Tarsus of hind leg: segment 2 shorter than segment 1 and 3 (segment 2 may be difficult to distinguish from segment 1) (fig. H3b,c); glossae as long as paraglossae (fig. H1a)—   **3**

—   Tarsus of hind leg: segment 3 much longer than segment 1 and 2 (fig. H3d); glossae reduced (fig. H1b)—   **6**

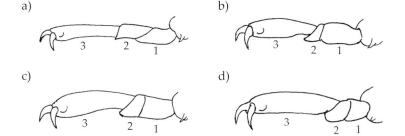

Fig. H3. Hind tarsus of: (a) Taeniopterygidae; (b) Nemouridae; (c) Leuctridae; (d) Perlodidae. Tarsal segments are numbered.

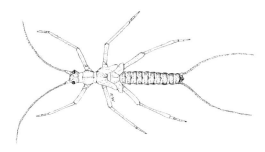

Fig. H4. Taeniopterygidae.

2 Horn-like extensions on the top of abdominal segments 1-7 (view from the side) (fig. H5a); the base of each leg has a segmented gill on the inner side (fig. H5b) — ***Taeniopteryx nebulosa***

Up to 12 mm long. The gills are 3-segmented and retractable into the thorax. Emergent vegetation of rivers, occasionally in moss, but usually in sedge, reeds or grass.

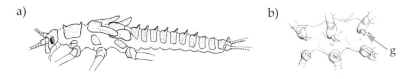

Fig. H5. *Taeniopteryx nebulosa*. (a) lateral view; (b) ventral view of thorax, showing a segmented gill, *g*, at the base of each leg.

— No horn-like extensions on abdomen; base of legs without gills; plate on 9th sternum (fig. H6) — ***Rhabdiopteryx acuminata*** and ***Brachyptera***

Rhabdiopteryx acuminata grows up to 10 mm long and is found in small calcareous rivers in Yorkshire. *Brachyptera* (2 species) grows up to 10 mm. One widespread species, *B. risi*, is found in small stony streams, occasionally in moss in rivers. *Brachyptera putata* is endemic to the UK; it is found in the slower reaches of Scottish rivers and until recently also occurred in Wales and adjacent parts of England. *Brachyptera* can be separated from *R. acuminata* by the presence of long hairs on the upper surface of the basal few segments of the tails.

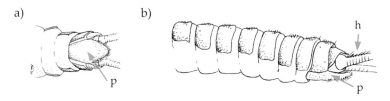

Fig. H6. *Brachyptera risi*. (a) end of abdomen (ventral view); (b) abdomen (lateral view). Plate, *p*, on sternum and hairs, *h*, on upper surface of tails arrowed.

3(1) Stout larvae with wing pads set obliquely to the body; hind legs considerably longer than abdomen (fig. H7a); in some species, gills (sausage-shaped or filamentous) are present on the underside of the pronotum— **Nemouridae: 4**

— Cylindrical elongate larvae with roughly parallel-sided wing buds; hind legs shorter than abdomen (fig. H8a, b); no gills— **5**

Note: This next 'couplet' has three end points
4 Underside of the prothorax (the 'neck') with three sausage-shaped gills on each side (fig. H7b)— *Protonemura*

Up to 10 mm long. 3 species. Small swift stony streams up to high altitudes.

— Underside of the prothorax with two bunches of 5-8 filamentous gills on each side (fig. H7c)— *Amphinemura*

Up to 6 mm long, typically covered with fine detritus. 2 species. Running water with a stony substratum; usually in larger streams and rivers.

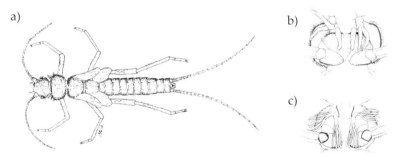

Fig. H7. Nemouridae. (a) whole animal, dorsal view; (b-c) ventral view of pronotum of: (b) *Protonemura*, giving examples of the range of angles in which the sausage-shaped gills may be lying; (c) *Amphinemura*.

— No gills present— ***Nemurella pictetii* and *Nemoura***

Up to 10 mm long. 6 species in *Nemoura*. Still or flowing waters, including relatively clean ditches.

5(3) Abdominal segments 1-9 with a clear division into dorsal (tergum) and ventral (sternum) sections; paraprocts wider than long (fig. H9a)—
Capniidae (fig. H8a)

Up to 9 mm long. 1 genus: *Capnia*; 3 species. Small stony streams and lake shores.

— Abdominal segments 1-4 only divided into tergum and sternum, segments 5-9 fused into complete rings (fig. H9b); paraprocts longer than wide — **Leuctridae** (fig. H8b)

Up to 11 mm long. 1 genus: *Leuctra*; 6 species. *Leuctra geniculata* is sometimes placed in a separate genus, *Euleuctra*. Stony streams and rivers.

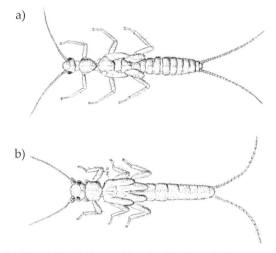

Fig. H8. (a) Capniidae; (b) Leuctridae; both in dorsal view.

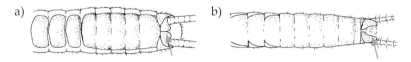

Fig. H9. Ventral view of abdomen, highlighting paraprocts, *pp*, of: (a) Capniidae; (b) Leuctridae.

6(1) Gills present on thorax (at base of legs)—   **Perlidae** (fig. H10a): **7**

—   No gills present on thorax—   **8**

7   Prothorax (first segment of the thorax) more than twice as wide as long;
    sub-mentum with anterior corners separated off by sutures (fig. H10b);
    last abdominal tergum uniformly dark—   *Dinocras cephalotes*

    Up to 35 mm long. Rivers with stable rocky and stony substrata; occasionally
    streams.

—   Prothorax less than twice as wide as long; anterior corners of sub-
    mentum not separated off by sutures (fig. H10c); last abdominal tergum
    yellow—   *Perla bipunctata*

    Up to 35 mm long. Rivers and streams with unstable stony substrata.

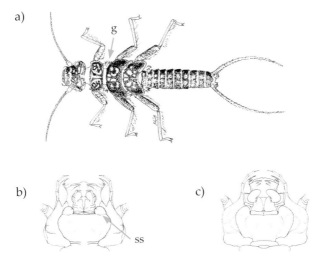

Fig. H10. Perlidae. (a) whole animal, dorsal view, with gills, *g* arrowed; (b-c)
ventral view of heads of: (b) *Dinocras cephalotes*, highlighting the suture, *ss*, in
the submentum; (c) *Perla bipunctata*.

8(6) Last segment of maxillary palp considerably smaller than the preceding segment (fig. H11a)—   **Chloroperlidae** (fig. H12)

Up to 12 mm long. 3 genera; 3 species, all formerly placed in a single genus: *Chloroperla*. The oval shape of each thoracic segment with wing buds (fig. H12) is distinctive in this family. Rivers and streams.

—   Last segment of maxillary palp similar in width to the preceding segment (fig. H11b)—   **Perlodidae** (fig. H13a): **9**

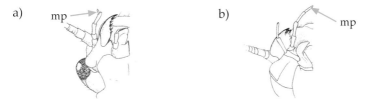

Fig. H11. Ventral view of one side of stonefly heads highlighting maxillary palp, *mp*, of: (a) Chloroperlidae; (b) Perlodidae.

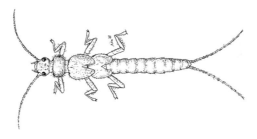

Fig. H12. Chloroperlidae, dorsal view.

9   First four abdominal segments clearly divided into upper (tergum) and lower (sternum) sections (fig. H13b)—   *Perlodes mortoni*

Up to 30 mm long. Formerly known as *P. microcephala*, but new evidence suggests that British (and probably Irish) populations are an endemic species, *P. mortoni*. Rivers and streams with stony substrata; occasionally on stony lake shores in Scotland.

—   Only first two abdominal segments divided into tergum and sternum (fig. H13c)—   **10**

a)

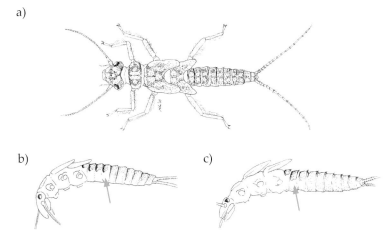

Fig. H13. Perlodidae. (a) whole animal, dorsal view; (b-c) lateral view of:
(b) *Perlodes*; (c) *Isoperla*, highlighting the division between tergum and sternum.

10   Paraprocts blunt (fig. H14a); body sparsely covered with scattered
     bristles—   ***Diura bicaudata*** and ***Isogenus nubecula***

Up to 21 mm long. *Diura bicaudata* is common in stony lake shores and stony
streams, normally at high altitudes. *Isogenus nubecula* is found in large stony
lowland rivers; recorded recently only from the Welsh Dee.

—   Paraprocts long and pointed (fig. H14b); body thickly covered with
     black clothing hairs—   ***Isoperla***

Up to 16 mm long. 2 species. *Isoperla grammatica* is very common, very
abundant, in stony streams and rivers; stony lake shores in the far north. *Isoperla
obscura* is very rare, possibly extinct.

Fig. H14. End of abdomen (ventral view) of: (a) *Diura*; (b) *Isoperla*.

Key I – Odonata

(Dragonflies and damselflies)

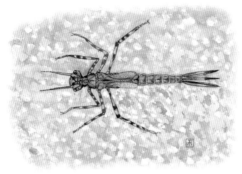

Calopteryx

The order Odonata divides naturally into two distinct suborders, the Anisoptera (dragonflies) and Zygoptera (damselflies). These groups are morphologically and behaviourally very different, but the distinguishing feature that they share is the presence of a mask (see fig. F1, page 74). This structure, on the ventral side of the head, is a greatly modified labium, part of the mouth of the animal. The base of the plate-like part of the mask is the prementum. The mask operates as a prey-capturing device: larval Odonata are predators that remain motionless or very slowly moving until a potential prey animal comes into range, when the mask is rapidly extended to capture it. The mask is unmistakeable but its form varies and this is used to distinguish different families of Odonata. Anisoptera include the larger members of the order; as adults they are strong flying insects compared to the smaller Zygoptera which have a relatively poor capacity for flight. At rest adult Anisoptera hold their wings open whereas Zygoptera hold theirs closed over the abdomen.

All Odonata larvae possess gills but the form of these is different and serves to separate the two suborders. The gills of Anisoptera are hidden within the rectum and it is the ability of the larva to pump water in and out of the anus that keeps these gills aerated. If water is pumped out with force, the larva is propelled forward; pumping water in and out in rapid succession results in a series of jerky movements which is characteristic of Anisoptera. In contrast, gills of Zygoptera are external and in the form of three leaf-like anal appendages (caudal lamellae), whose structure is important in distinguishing different species. Zygoptera larvae swim by moving their bodies from side to side, with the caudal lamellae acting as oars.

The Key

1   Slender in appearance (fig. I1a); abdomen terminating in three leaf-like appendages (fig. I2a) (N.B. these may drop off, leaving two, one or none)—   **ZYGOPTERA** (damselflies): **2**

—   Stout in appearance (fig. I1b); abdomen terminating in five short spine-like appendages (fig. I2b)—   **ANISOPTERA** (dragonflies): **5**

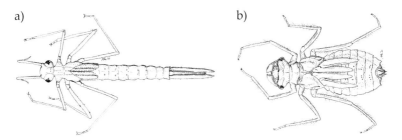

Fig. I1. Examples of Odonata larvae in dorsal view: (a) Zygoptera (Calopterygidae); (b) Anisoptera (Corduliidae).

Fig. I2. Posterior end of: (a) Zygoptera (showing caudal lamellae) (lateral view); (b) Anisoptera (showing appendages) (dorsal view).

2 Antennae with basal segment (scape) as long as the combined length of the remaining segments (fig. I3a)— **Calopterygidae (demoiselles)**

Up to 25 mm long. 1 genus: *Calopteryx*; 2 species. Largely restricted to running waters.

— Antennae with scape much less than the combined length of the remaining segments (fig. I3b)— 3

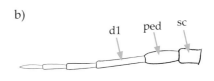

Fig. I3. (a) Dorsal view of head of Calopterygidae, with scape shaded and arrowed; (b) antenna of Coenagriidae with scape, *sc*, pedicel, *ped* and distalia 1, *d1* arrowed.

3 [Note: To separate the following three families you will need to pull out the mask and look at its overall shape and various features.]
Prementum of mask with a long stem, forming a Y shape; median lobe with a slit in the middle (median cleft) (fig. I4a)—
Lestidae (emerald damselflies)

Up to 25 mm long. 2 genera; 5 species. Standing and slow-flowing vegetated waters; lie partially buried in mud.

— Prementum of mask without a long stem; median lobe without median cleft (fig. I4b)— 4

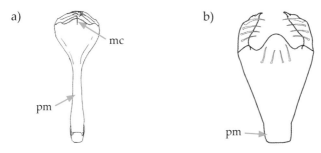

Fig. I4. Labium of: (a) Lestidae, showing long stem of prementum, *pm* and median cleft, *mc*; (b) Platycnemididae, showing short stem of prementum, *pm*.

4   Third segment (distalia 1) of antennae longer than second segment (pedicel) (fig. I3b); narrow point on end of lamellae not on a long extension (fig. I5a)— **Coenagrionidae**

Up to 27 mm long. 6 genera; 12 species. Mainly standing waters amongst plants.

—   Third segment of antennae shorter than second segment; long narrow point present on end of lamellae (fig. I5b)— **Platycnemididae**

Up to 20 mm long. 1 species: *Platycnemis pennipes*. Prefers slow-flowing vegetated rivers and streams. Currently restricted to the southern half of England.

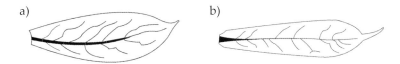

a)   b)

Fig. I5. Caudal lamella of: (a) Coenagrionidae; (b) Platycnemididae.

5(1) Larva with a flat mask which is not obvious when viewed from the front (fig. I6a)— 6

—   Larva with a spoon-shaped mask which is distinct when viewed from the front, and covers the front of the face (fig. I6b)— 7

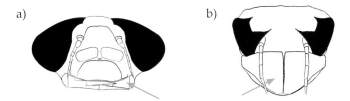

a)   b)

Fig. I6. Dragonfly heads viewed from the front: (a) a flat mask (arrowed); (b) a spoon-shaped mask (arrowed).

6   Antennae with seven segments—   **Aeshnidae (hawkers)**

Up to 55 mm long. 4 genera; 12 species. Dense vegetation in standing and
running waters.

—   Antennae with four segments—   **Gomphidae**

Up to 30 mm long. 1 genus: *Gomphus*; 2 species. Slow-flowing rivers and muddy
lake shores. Lie partially buried in mud.

7(5) Mask with jagged, irregular serrations and bifid (double-peaked)
     medial lobe (fig. I7a)—   **Cordulegastridae**

Up to 45 mm long. 1 species: *Cordulegaster boltonii* (golden-ringed dragonfly).
Running waters, including acid streams. Lies partially buried in mud.

—   Mask with slight regular serrations; median lobe with a single peak
     (fig. I7b)—   **8**

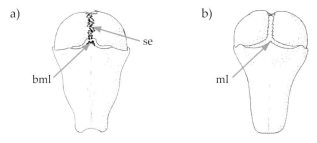

Fig. I7. Ventral view of labium of: (a) Cordulegastridae, jagged serrations, *se* and
bifid median lobe, *bml*, arrowed; (b) Corduliidae, median lobe, *ml*, arrowed.

8   Cerci at posterior end of abdomen more than half the length of the paraprocts (fig. I8a); front of mask with broad deep indentations (fig. I9a)—   **Corduliidae**

Up to 30 mm long. 2 genera; 3 species. Standing and slow-flowing waters.

—   Cerci less than half the length of the paraprocts (fig. I8b); front of mask with shallow indentations (fig. I9b)—   **Libellulidae**

Up to 25 mm long. 6 genera; 17 species. Standing and slow-flowing waters.

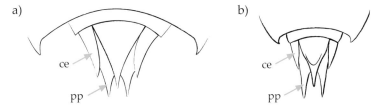

Fig. I8. Rear appendages of: (a) Corduliidae; (b) Libellulidae, highlighting cerci, *ce* and paraprocts, *pp*.

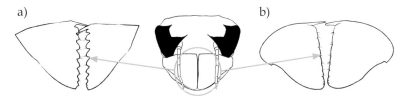

Fig. I9. Front of mask of: (a) Corduliidae; (b) Libellulidae.

Key J – Hemiptera
(True bugs)

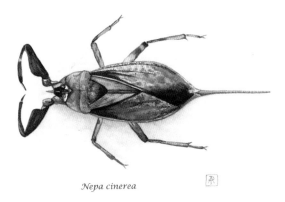

Nepa cinerea

All bugs have mouthparts which are fused into a tube-like, piercing and sucking rostrum or beak. They are divisible by habit into two main groups: surface dwellers, which have prominent antennae, and sub-surface dwellers, which have reduced antennae. Wings are often absent but where present they overlap asymmetrically (e.g. fig. J9), often giving the appearance of a cross on the back. These features distinguish them from beetles, which have biting mouthparts and hardened wing cases (elytra) that are always present in adults, normally cover the entire abdomen and are clearly symmetrical, meeting in a straight line down the back.

This key is designed for identifying adults. However, juveniles generally resemble miniature adults, lacking only developed genitalia, wings and elytra, which develop as the bug moults and grows in size. The similarity between the juveniles and adults in their appearance and habit should be sufficient to enable the identification of most juveniles using this key.

The Key

Note: All figures of whole animals are in dorsal view unless otherwise stated.

1   Obvious antennae, much longer than the head; animals occur on the water surface (e.g. fig. J1)—   **2**

—   Antennae not obvious and not visible when viewed from above, much shorter than the head and hidden in ventral pits; animals occur under the water (e.g. fig. J6)—   **6**

2   Head very long and narrow, many times longer than wide; eyes situated approximately half way along the head, some distance from the front margin of the pronotum—

Hydrometridae (water measurer) (fig. J1)

Up to 12 mm long. 1 genus (*Hydrometra*); 2 species. Walk on water surface with all six legs. Wingless, but rudimentary wing covers present.

—   Head no more than 3x as long as wide; eyes towards the back of the head—   **3**

3   All legs originate near the centre line of the body (fig. J2b)—

Mesoveliidae (fig. J2a)

Up to 4 mm long. 1 species: *Mesovelia furcata*. Usually wingless. Uncommon.

—   Legs, particularly the hind legs, originate towards, or at, the margins of the body (as in figs J4b, J5b)—   **4**

4   Antennae with five segments, the last three segments being more slender than the two closest to the head; ocelli (small eyespots between the eyes) present—   **Hebridae** (fig. J3)

 Up to 2 mm long. 1 genus (*Hebrus*); 2 species. Amongst vegetation at the edges of ponds and lakes.

—   Antennae with four segments, all segments approximately equal in thickness (e.g. fig. 4a); ocelli absent—   **5**

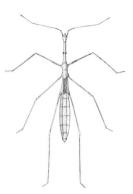

Fig. J1. Hydrometridae.

a)   b)

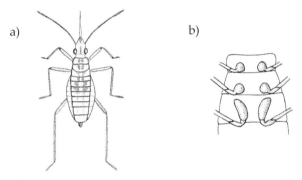

Fig. J2. Mesoveliidae: (a) whole animal; (b) ventral view of thorax.

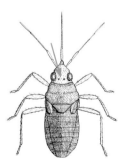

Fig. J3. Hebridae, with ocelli arrowed.

107

5   Middle legs originate approximately midway between the front and
     rear legs (fig. J4b); rear femur not extending beyond the tip of the
     abdomen—   **Veliidae (water cricket)** (fig. J4a)

Up to 8 mm long. 2 genera; 5 species. Still parts of rivers and streams; run or
walk over the water surface with all six legs.

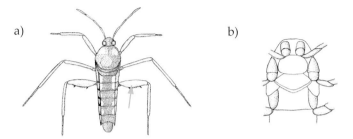

Fig. J4. Veliidae: (a) whole animal, with femur arrowed; (b) ventral view of
thorax.

—   Middle legs originate much closer to the rear legs than the front ones
     (fig. J5b); rear femur extends well beyond the tip of the abdomen—
                          Gerridae (pond skater or water strider) (fig. J5a)

Up to 18 mm long. 3 genera; 10 species. Move across water surface by rowing or
jumping on the tips of the middle and rear legs.

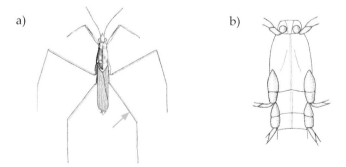

Fig. J5. Gerridae: (a) whole animal, with femur arrowed; (b) ventral view of
thorax.

6(1) Head with a short broad rostrum which is tucked underneath (fig. J6b); tarsi of front legs often flattened with only one segment; scutellum (triangular plate between bases of wings) hidden by the wing cases (except in the very small *Micronecta*: max. size 2.5 mm)—
Corixidae (lesser water boatman) (fig. J6a)

Up to 15 mm long. 9 genera; 37 species. Swim quickly under the water; males of some species produce a sound like a cricket.

a)　　　　　　　　　　　　　b)

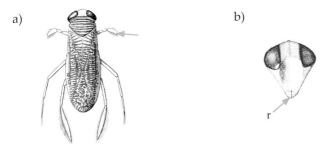

Fig. J6. Corixidae: (a) whole animal, with tarsus arrowed; (b) anterior view of head, with rostrum, *r*, arrowed.

— Head with an obvious, pointed rostrum, often extending from the front of the head (e.g. figs J7, J10); tarsi of front legs never flattened and rarely with one segment; scutellum visible and not hidden by the wing cases (figs J7, J8)— 　7

7 Two long appendages at the rear of the body, usually held together to form a single tube for respiration (figs J7, J8); crawlers, without swimming hairs on the legs— **Nepidae: 8**

Up to 35 mm long (excluding respiratory tube). Dense vegetation in shallow water. Front legs modified for grasping prey.

— No rear appendages; swimmers, with rows of swimming hairs on rear legs— 　9

8   Body oval in outline when viewed from above and flattened when
     viewed from the side—   ***Nepa cinerea*** (water scorpion) (fig. J7)

—   Body long and narrow in outline when viewed from above and
     cylindrical—   ***Ranatra linearis*** **(water stick insect)** (fig. J8)

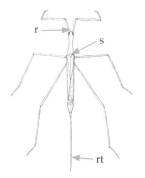

Fig. J7. *Nepa cinerea* with rostrum, *r*, scutellum, *s*, and respiratory tube, *rt*, arrowed.

Fig. J8. *Ranatra linearis* with rostrum, *r*, scutellum, *s*, and respiratory tube, *rt*, arrowed.

9(7) Body flattened when viewed from the side, oval in outline when viewed
     from above; animals swim with topside uppermost; front legs originate
     on the front margin of the pronotum—   **10**

—   Body boat-shaped when viewed from the side, not oval in outline when
     viewed from above; animals swim with underside uppermost; front
     legs originate on the rear margin of the pronotum—   **11**

10   Head wider than long; rostrum relatively short, reaching the base of the front legs when folded under the body; femora of front legs very wide, with tibia folded against them; always winged —   **Naucoridae** (fig. J9)

Up to 15 mm long. 2 species: *Ilyocoris cimicoides* is found in ponds mainly in southern England. *Naucoris maculatus* has been recorded from the Channel Islands.

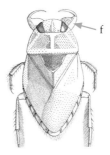

Fig. J9. Naucoridae: *Ilyocoris cimicoides* with femur, *f*, arrowed.

—   Head as wide as long; rostrum relatively long, reaching the base of the rear legs when folded under the body; femora of the front legs not as above; usually wingless, although some winged specimens have been found in the River Severn —   **Aphelocheiridae** (fig. J10)

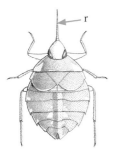

Up to 10 mm long. 1 species: *Aphelocheirus aestivalis*. Fast flowing rivers, often in the deepest parts. This species has a plastron (a thin film of air around the body surface, retained in position by fine setae, which is used as a source of oxygen) and is the only bug that can survive underwater, without visiting the surface, as an adult.

Fig. J10. Aphelocheiridae: *Aphelocheirus aestivalis* with rostrum, *r*, arrowed.

11(9)Pronotum and wing covers pitted; tarsi with three segments; body shape semicircular in outline when viewed from the side—

Pleidae (fig. J11)

Up to 3 mm long. 1 species: *Plea minutissima,* formerly known as *P. leachi.* Ponds mainly in southern England.

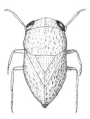

Fig. J11. Pleidae: *Plea minutissima.*

— Pronotum and wing covers smooth; tarsi with two segments; body shape elliptical/tear drop shaped in outline when viewed from the side—   **Notonectidae (greater water boatman)** (fig. J12)

Up to 16 mm long. 1 genus (*Notonecta*); 4 species. Still waters.

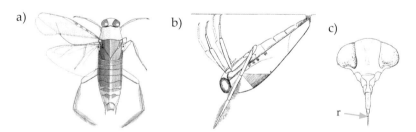

Fig. J12.Notonectidae: (a) whole animal; (b) lateral view; (c) anterior view of head, with rostrum, *r,* arrowed.

Key K – Trichoptera

(Caddisflies)

Limnephilidae

Caddisflies (sometimes referred to simply as 'caddis') are generally divided into 'cased' and 'caseless' species, depending upon whether their larvae construct a transportable case. Although this distinction usually works well, it is complicated when cased species abandon their cases. Some species do this only in exceptional circumstances, but can often be found without their cases in preserved samples; others, particularly Glossosomatidae and Phryganeidae, will leave their cases more readily. One family, the Hydroptilidae, is caseless in all but its final larval stage. Therefore, the presence or otherwise of a case has not been used as an identification feature in the following key below. Most caseless species build a silken tube or web in which they live, although one family, the Rhyacophilidae, are active, free-living predators. To assist with identification, tables K1 and K2 are given at the end of the key listing the types of cases or spun structures possessed by each family. It is worth noting that all caddisflies pupate within a case, 'caseless' species constructing one for this purpose which they attach to rocks or vegetation.

All caddisfly larvae have a pair of widely spaced hooks at the posterior end of the abdomen, attached to anal prolegs. Among most cased species these prolegs are short (e.g. figs K8b, K12a), whereas among caseless species they are long and clearly visible (e.g. figs K9a K10a). Most cased species have

113

two or three swellings on the first abdominal segment, which help to secure the case, whereas these are never present in caseless species; note, however, that these swellings are not always clear as they may collapse in preserved specimens.

Differentiation of caddisfly larvae, even to family level, often relies on features that, until you become familiar with the general layout of a caddisfly larva, may prove difficult to locate and often need good lighting and magnification to see. The location and size of hardened (sclerotised) parts of the thorax is particularly diagnostic for many families. The three segments of the thorax are the prothorax (closest to the head), mesothorax and metathorax; the terms 'prodorsum', 'mesodorsum' and 'metadorsum' are often used to specify that the dorsal side of these segments is being referred to, while the term 'prosternal', referring to the underside of the prothorax, is used at one point in the key below. Where the dorsal surface of the thoracic segments have hardened plates, these are referred to as nota (singular: notum), so the plate on the first segment of the thorax is called the pronotum, and the others are the mesonotum and metanotum. The prodorsum is always hardened, but whether the dorsal surface of each of the other thoracic segments is completely hardened (sclerotised) or soft (membranous) is an important distinguishing feature, as is whether soft dorsal areas are completely membranous or have small hardened plates (sclerites). The sclerotised areas and discrete sclerites *normally*, but not always, appear darker than the membranous areas (prodding with forceps will confirm whether a hardened plate is present), and may be patterned. The arrangement of sclerites on the metadorsum (e.g. fig. K16) is a useful diagnostic feature among some groups. A single sclerite may also be found on the dorsal side of the last (ninth) abdominal segment, and this again is a diagnostic feature for some groups.

Other features are required to differentiate specific groups of families, and these are referred to where appropriate in the key. Features such as abdominal gills and swellings on the first abdominal segment may not be as obvious in some specimens as they appear on the diagrams, so bear this in mind when looking for them.

The term 'setae' is used to describe hair-like structures. True hairs are found only on mammals.

Note: all illustrations of whole animals are in lateral view, unless otherwise stated.

Key to larvae

Note: This 'couplet' has three end points

1 Prodorsum, mesodorsum and metadorsum are each covered by
hardened plates (both cased and caseless families) (figs K1a, K5a)— **2**

— Prodorsum with hardened plates, mesodorsum and metadorsum are
soft or not completely hardened (small, widely separated sclerites may
be present) (both cased and caseless families) (fig. K1b). Note: if plates
on mesodorsum are relatively large and close together, but cover no
more than half of the mesodorsum, as in fig. K7a, choose this option— **6**

— Prodorsum and mesodorsum with hardened plates (include those
where the mesodorsum is largely or almost entirely covered by discrete
plates); metadorsum soft (although small, widely separated sclerites
may be present) (only cased families) (fig. K1c)— **14**

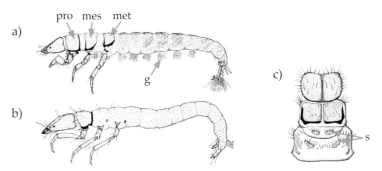

Fig K1. Examples of caddisfly larvae: a) Hydropsychidae, showing hardened
prodorsum, *pro*, mesodorsum, *mes*, and metadorsum, *met*, plus tufted gills,
g; (b) Philopotamidae, with unsclerotised mesodorsum and metadorsum;
(c) thorax of Limnephilidae, dorsal view, showing sclerites, *s*, on metadorsum.

2 Tufted gills on the underside of the abdomen (fig. K1a)—
Hydropsychidae: 3

Up to 20 mm long. 3 genera. Prolegs at posterior end of body with a thick brush of
long bristles. Caseless, net-spinning (fig. K4a). Fairly fast flowing water.

— Abdomen without gills, although there may be a fringe of setae— **5**

3 Pronotum with a dense covering of long setae on the front edge, clearly visible when viewed from the side (fig. K2a)— *Cheumatopsyche lepida*

Up to 10 mm long. Lower reaches of large rivers and outflows of lakes.

— Pronotum without a dense covering of setae (fig. K2b)— **4**

4 Dorsal surface of the head with distinctive patterning (fig. K2c)—
Hydropsyche

Up to 20 mm long. 9 species. *Hydropsyche siltalai* has six pairs of abdominal gills (fig. K1a); all other species have seven pairs (do not count the two pairs of thoracic gills, between the legs). Fast flowing water.

— Dorsal surface of head uniformly brown— *Diplectrona felix*

Up to 15 mm long. This is the only British hydropsychid apart from *Hydropsyche siltalai* (described above) to have only six pairs of abdominal gills. Headwater streams.

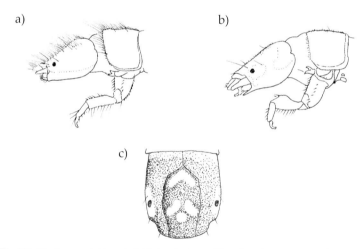

Fig K2. Hydropsychidae: (a-b) lateral view of head and pronotum of a) *Cheumatopsyche*; (b) *Hydropsyche*; (c) dorsal view of head of *Hydropsyche*.

5(2) Abdomen with a distinct fringe of lateral setae (best seen in profile); rear of abdomen tapering (fig. K3)—   **Ecnomidae**

Up to 12 mm long. 1 genus; 1 species: *Ecnomus tenellus*. Caseless, in silken tube. Lakes and slow flowing waters, particularly canals with loose boulder reinforcements.

— Abdomen without lateral setae; abdomen distinctly swollen (fig. K5a)—   **Hydroptilidae**

Up to 6 mm long. 7 genera; 31 species. Case-building; but caseless in early stages. The case is made of silk, often embedded with fine particles (fig. K5b), and consists of two similar halves. Most types of water body.

a)   b)

Fig K3 Ecnomidae – *Ecnomus tenellus*: a) whole animal, with fringe of setae arrowed; (b) ventral view of abdomen, showing fringe of setae visible in profile.

a)   b)

Fig. K4. Examples of nets spun by caseless caddisfly larvae: a) Hydropsychidae, showing animal in net; b) Psychomyiidae galleries fixed to surface of submerged wood.

a)   b)

Fig. K5. Hydroptilidae: (a) whole animal; (b) example of case.

6(1) Tufted lateral gills on the abdomen (fig. K8a)— **Rhyacophilidae**

Up to 25 mm long. 1 genus: *Rhyacophila*; 4 species. Caseless and free-living, without swellings on first abdominal segment. Some species in mainland Europe lack gills, but are distinguished from Glossosomatidae by their long posterior prolegs and the absence of plates on the thoracic segments. All species in this family are in the same genus, *Rhyacophila*, and one species *Rhyacophila munda*, is distinctive in that the gills on the thorax, at the base of the legs, have only one filament, whilst those on the segments of the abdomen have four. In the three remaining species, the gills on both the thorax and the abdomen have multiple filaments. Fast flowing water.

—   No tufted gills (although gills consisting of single filaments may be present)— 7

7   Hardened plate present on the upper surface of the ninth (last) abdominal segment (as in fig. K6a, a feature shared with Rhyacophilidae); may have obvious gills on abdomen— 8

—   No hardened plate on the upper surface of the ninth (last) abdominal segment (fig. K6b)— 10

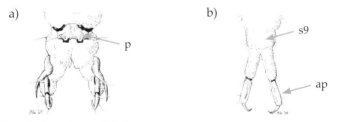

Fig. K6. Dorsal view of rear of abdomen of: (a) Rhyacophilidae, showing hardened plate, *p*; (b) Polycentropodidae, with 9th abdominal segment, *s9*, and sclerotised section of anal proleg, *ap*, arrowed.

8   Abdomen without gills (fig. K7a) —   **Glossosomatidae: 9**

Up to 10 mm long. 3 genera. Large plates present on the side of each thoracic segment, immediately above the leg attachment (fig. K7b). Case-building: making a rounded, relatively fragile case from large mineral particles with an equal-sized aperture at each end, the case being fixed to a solid surface (fig. K7c, d). Stony streams and occasionally stony lake shores. Some species of Rhyacophilidae in mainland Europe lack gills, but are distinguished from Glossosomatidae by their long posterior prolegs and the absence of plates on the thoracic segments.

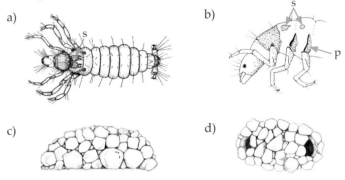

Fig. K7. Glossosomatidae: (a), dorsal view of whole animal with sclerites, *s*, on mesodorsum arrowed; (b) lateral view of anterior part of *Agapetus*, with the large plates, *p*, and hardened sclerites, *s*, arrowed; (c) case in lateral view; (d) case in ventral view, showing anterior and posterior apertures.

—   Long filamentous gills on the abdomen, held close to the body
      (fig. K8b) —   **Phryganeidae**

Up to 40 mm long. 6 genera; 10 species. Distinctive lateral swellings present on first abdominal segment. Most species have distinct dark bands on the head. Case-building: constructing a case from neatly arranged detritus or plant stems (fig. K8c), often arranged in a spiral (fig. K8d). Still and slow flowing water, including salt marsh edges.

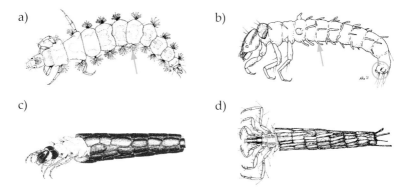

Fig. K8. (a) Rhyacophilidae, dorsal view; (b) Phryganeidae, with location of anal prolegs circled; arrows point to examples of gills of each family; (c,d) examples of cases of Phryganeidae: (c) case made from large pieces cut from dead leaves; (d) case made from plant fragments arranged in a spiral.

9   Hardened sclerites present in the middle of the mesodorsum and metadorsum (fig. K7a, b)—   **Agapetinae**

   2 genera (*Agapetus*, *Synagapetus*); 4 species. *Synagapetus* (1 species, *Synagapetus dubitans*) was first recorded in Britain in 2010.

—   No hardened sclerites on mesodorsum or metadorsum—
        Glossosomatinae

1 genus: *Glossosoma*; 3 species.

10(7) Labrum (plate at front edge of the head) hardened and pigmented (the same colour as, or darker than, the head capsule) (fig. K11a)—   **13**

—   Labrum either apparently absent or pale and membranous (in contrast to the darker colour of the head capsule; make sure you are looking at the labrum and not the front margin of the head itself) (fig. K9)—
        Philopotamidae: 11

Up to 25 mm long. 3 genera. The basal membranous section of the anal proleg is equal in length to the sclerotised section. The head lacks dark markings. Caseless. Fast flowing water, typically the rapids of small streams.

11   Frontoclypeus (front edge of the head capsule) has a smooth, unbroken outline (fig. K9b)—   ***Wormaldia*** (3 species)

—   Frontoclypeus with indent in its outline (fig. K9c,d)—   **12**

12   Indent in frontoclypeus outline irregular, deep and U shaped (fig. K9c)—   ***Chimarra marginata***

—   Indent in frontoclypeus outline irregular, shallow and more V shaped (fig. K9d)—   ***Philopotamus montanus***

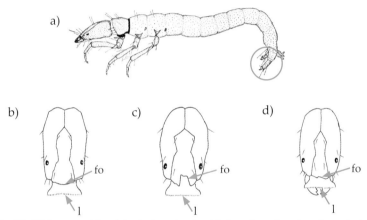

Fig. K9. Philopotamidae: (a) whole animal, with location of anal prolegs circled; (b-d) dorsal view of head, with extended labrum, *l*, and frontoclypeus outline, *fo*, arrowed: (b) *Wormaldia*; (c) *Chimarra*; (d) *Philopotamus*.

13(10) Anal proleg with one clear sclerotised section (the unsclerotised basal section is not obvious) (fig. K10b); underside of each femur with only sparse setae— **Psychomyiidae** (fig. K10a)

Up to 10 mm long. 4 genera; 12 species. Caseless, living in galleries. Species in the genus *Lype* build galleries on rotting wood (fig. K4b), upon which they feed. Streams, in slow flowing water and stony lakes.

One species is distinct: *Tinodes waeneri* has a frontoclypeal apotome which is much darker than the rest of the head, and a mostly darkened prodorsum with obvious pale oval patches on each side of the midline (fig. K10c,d).

— Anal proleg with two sections of roughly equal length (the rear section is sclerotised) (fig. K6b); underside of each femur with many long setae— **Polycentropodidae** (fig. K11b)

Up to 25 mm long. 5 genera; 13 species. Caseless. Occur in both still and flowing water. Sometimes referred to as Polycentropidae.

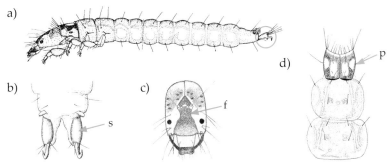

Fig. K10. Psychomyiidae: (a) whole animal, with location of anal prolegs circled; (b) posterior of abdomen, dorsal view, with sclerotised section, *s*, arrowed; (c) head, with the frontoclypeal apotome, *f*, arrowed; (d) thorax of *Tinodes waeneri*, dorsal view, with prodorsum, *p*, arrowed.

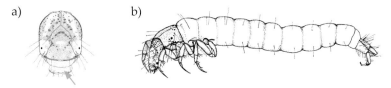

Fig. K11. Polycentropodidae: (a) dorsal view of head, with labrum, arrowed; (b) whole animal.

14(1)Hardened mesodorsum consists of a series of plates, of which those on the lateral edges have distinct forward-facing extensions (fig. K12b)—
Goeridae (fig. K12a)

Up to 13 mm long. 2 genera (*Goera, Silo*); 3 species. Case-building: the strong case is made from mineral particles and edged with a distinctive 'keel' of much larger ballast stones (fig. K12c). Fig. F6b, page 78, shows a case of *Silo* that has been parasitised by the ichneumoid wasp *Agriotypus armatus*. Fast-flowing running waters and gravelly lake shores.

The genera can be distinguished by the shape of the mesolateral sclerite on the mesodorsum. This is bluntly-pointed in *Goera pilosa* (fig. K12d), but round-ended in the two species of *Silo* (fig. K12e).

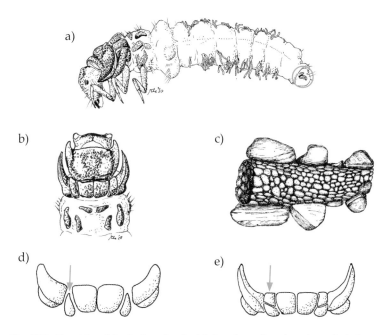

Fig. K12. Goeridae: (a) whole animal with location of anal prolegs circled; (b) dorsal view of head and thorax; (c) case; (d,e) sclerites on mesodorsum of: (d) *Goera*, and (e) *Silo*, with the mesolateral sclerite arrowed.

—   Mesodorsum without distinct forward-facing extensions—   **15**

15   Sclerites on metadorsum arranged as in figs K15b or K16; underside of the prothorax with a horn (prosternal horn) (fig. K13)—   **16**

—   Sclerites on metadorsum arranged as in figs K21b, K23d, or very small and indistinct, or absent; prosternal horn absent—   **18**

Fig. K13. Ventral view of head and thorax of Lepidostomatidae, with prosternal horn arrowed.

16   Underside of the head consists of three sections (fig. K14a); dorsal swelling present on first segment of the abdomen (fig. K17a) (although the swelling may have been compacted, it should still be visible when viewed from above)—   **17**

—   Underside of the head consists of five sections, as the gena (the main part of the underside) has a distinct fold on each side (fig. K14b); no dorsal swelling on first abdominal segment (fig. K15a), but lateral swellings may be visible—   **Lepidostomatidae**

Up to 11 mm long. 3 genera; 3 species. Posterior edge of mesodorsum with a line of forward-facing bristles. It is possible to differentiate the larvae of this family from all other caddisflies except Limnephilidae by the arrangement of the sclerotised plates on the metadorsum (fig. K15b; compare with K16b). Case-building: the case is initially made from sand grains or detritus and is circular in cross-section, but the most common species usually change to detritus, square in cross-section (fig. K15c), as they get older, leading to a mixed-material case (fig. K15d) unique to this family. *Brachycentrus subnubilis* (couplet 19, fig. K21) is the only other species that constructs a case square in cross-section. Running waters and lake shores.

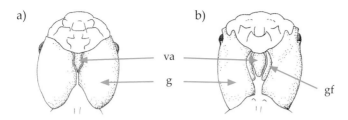

Fig. K14. Underside of head of: (a) Limnephilidae, showing three sections – the ventral apotome, *va*, and left and right gena, *g*; (b) Lepidostomatidae, showing five sections created by the presence of the genal fold, *gf*.

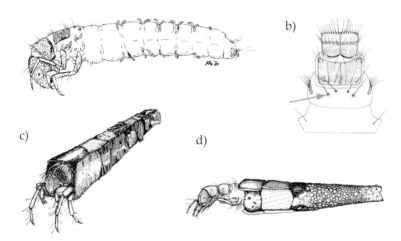

Fig. K15. Lepidostomatidae: (a) whole animal; (b) thorax, dorsal view, with sclerites arrowed; (c) animal in case; (d) animal in case made from mixed materials.

17 One or two hardened sclerites present on the anterior side of the metadorsum (fig. K16a-c)— **Limnephilidae** (fig. K17a)

Up to 25 mm long. 20 genera; 55 species. Case-building: a wide variety of cases made from sand, detritus and other materials, sometimes in combination, seldom regular in structure (fig. K17b-h). A wide range of habitats from trickles and streams to lakes and temporary water bodies.

— No hardened sclerites on the anterior side of the metadorsum, although long setae are present (fig. K16d)— **Apataniidae**

Up to 12 mm long. 1 genus: *Apatania*; 4 species. Until recently considered a part of the Limnephilidae. Case-building: case made from small mineral particles, tapering and slightly curved (fig. K18). Small stony streams and lake shores.

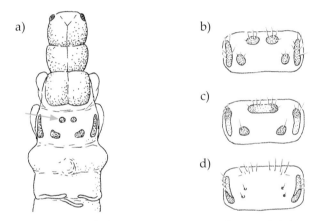

Fig. K16. Arrangement of sclerites on metadorsum of Limnephilidae and Apataniidae: (a) dorsal view of anterior half of Limnephilidae, with anterior sclerites of the metadorsum arrowed. (b-e) arrangements of sclerites on the metadorsum of: (b) Limnephilidae (most genera); (c) Limnephilidae (*Hydratophylax infumatus* only); (d) Apataniidae.

18(15) Tibia of one or more pairs of legs has a distinct downward-pointing protuberance ending in a spine (fig. K19a, b)— **19**

— All tibiae without distinct protuberance (a spine may be present, as in fig. K19c, but not on a protuberance)— **20**

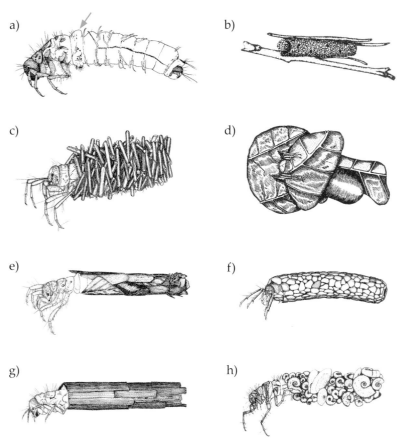

Fig. K17. Limnephilidae: (a) whole animal, with dorsal swelling arrowed; (b-h) examples of cases.

Fig. K18 Apataniidae in case.

19   Downward-pointing protuberance on the tibia of the first pair of legs
      only (fig. K19a)—   **Molannidae** (fig. K20a)

Up to 18 mm long. 1 genus: *Molanna*; 2 species. The two species can be separated
by looking at the head pattern. The rear part of the frontoclypeal apotome
(the central section of the head: fig. K20b) is dark in *M. albicans* and pale in *M.
angustata*.

A unique feature of this family is the presence of multiple spines on the claws
of the hind legs. Case-building: the distinctive shield-shaped case with a central
tube (fig. K20c, d) is made from fine mineral or detritus particles. Still and slow
flowing water.

—   Downward-pointing protuberance on the tibia of the second and third
      pair of legs only (fig. K19b)—   **Brachycentridae** (fig. K21a)

Up to 18 mm. 1 species: *Brachycentrus subnubilis*. Typically greenish in colour
when alive. Sclerites on the metadorsum are of equal size and arranged in
a semi-circle, and there is a distinctive transverse ridge on the pronotum
(fig. K21b). Case-building: case initially square in cross-section (the only species
building a case in this shape other than some Lepidostomatidae [couplet 16
fig. K15]) and constructed of transversely arranged pieces of plant material;
older larvae create cases almost entirely of secretion and circular in cross-
section (fig. K21c). Large streams and rivers, usually associated with submerged
vegetation to which the cases are fixed. Has an unusual feeding method of
extending legs to catch passing objects.

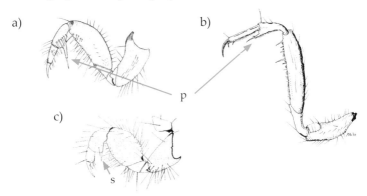

Fig. K19. (a) 1st leg of Molannidae; (b) 2nd leg of Brachycentridae; (c) 1st leg
of Leptoceridae, with the spine, s, arrowed. The protuberance, *p*, on the tibia is
arrowed.

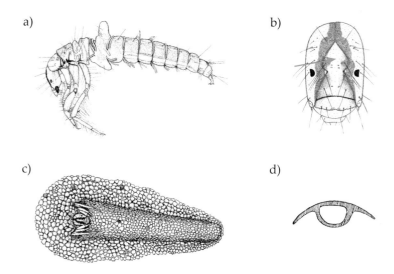

Fig. K20. Molannidae (*Molanna angustata*): (a) whole animal; (b) head of *Molanna angustata*, with the frontoclypeal apotome arrowed; (c) animal in case, ventral view; (d) case in anterior view.

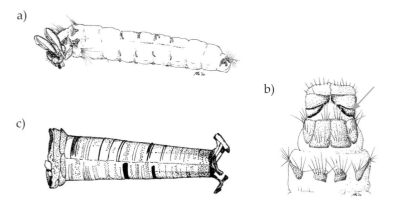

Fig. K21. Brachycentridae (*Brachycentrus subnubilis*): (a) whole animal; (b) thorax, dorsal view, showing transverse ridge on pronotum, arrowed, and arrangement of sclerites on metadorsum; (c) case of older larva.

20(18) A distinctive forward-facing flap present on each side of the pronotum (fig. K22b); a pair of long thick backward-pointing setae at the rear of the abdomen (fig. K22c)—

Beraeidae – part (fig. K22a): **all except** *Beraeodes*
(keyed out at couplet 22)

Up to 10 mm long. 3 genera; 4 species (including *Beraeodes minutus*). Case-building: curved and tapering case made from sand grains (fig. K22d). Head often red or orange in later instars. Flowing marshes, trickles and springs.

a)   b)

c)   d)

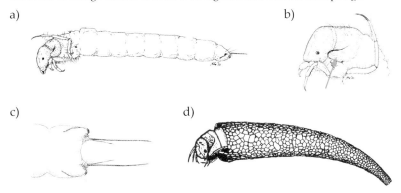

Fig. K22. Beraeidae: (a) whole animal; (b) head and prothorax, with flap arrowed; (c) long, thick, backward-pointing bristles; (d) case.

—   Neither of these features present—   **21**

21   Third (hind) pair of legs appreciably longer than the front two pairs (figs K24a, K26a); claw on rear proleg with a main hook and one or more additional smaller hooks (fig. K25a, b)—   **22**

—   Third pair of legs not appreciably longer than the other pairs; claw on anal proleg with a single hook (fig. K25c, d)— **Odontoceridae** (fig. K23a)

Up to 18 mm long. 1 species: *Odontocerum albicorne*. Normally a distinctive X-mark (or anchor mark) on head (fig. K23c). Case-building: a very strong curved case made from sand gains and with a larger stone blocking the rear end (fig. K23b), which can be dislodged and is sometimes therefore absent. Front edges of prothorax form a blunt point and arrangement of sclerites distinctive (fig. K23d). Stony streams and rivers.

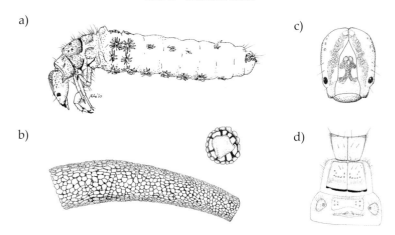

Fig. K23. Odontoceridae (*Odontocerum albicorne*): (a) whole animal; (b) case, highlighting large stone at posterior end; (c) head, showing distinctive X-mark (or anchor mark); (d) sclerites on thorax.

22 Fringe of setae on the front of the head; mosaic of distinctive black spots on the pronotum during the final instar (fig. K24b)—
Beraeidae – part: *Beraeodes minutus* (fig. K24a)

Up to 10 mm long. Case-building: curved and tapering case made from sand grains (fig. K24c). Submerged roots of emergent vegetation.

This species is distinct from the other three species in the same family, and does not possess the features which characterise them; it is more like Leptoceridae, with a very long third pair of legs.

— No fringe of setae on the front of the head; pronotum lacking distinctive black spots— **23**

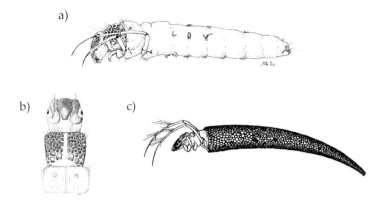

Fig. K24. Beraeidae: *Beraeodes minutus*: (a) whole animal; (b) dorsal view of head and thorax; (c) animal in case.

23   Head capsule uniformly dark or with pale patterning—
Sericostomatidae (fig. K27a)

Up to 17 mm long. 2 genera; 2 species. Meso- and metadorsum with lines of forward-facing, long setae. Case-building: constructs a curved case of fine mineral particles (fig. K27c). Still and flowing water.

The species are distinguishable by looking at the anterior corner of the prothorax. In *Sericostoma personatum* it is extruded into a sharp point (fig. K27b), whilst in *Notidobia ciliaris* it is rounded.

—   Head case either pale or distinctly patterned—   **Leptoceridae** (fig. K26a)

Up to 15 mm long. 10 genera, 31 species. Each lateral swelling of the first abdominal segment supports a hardened sclerite. Some species possess a pair of dark stripes on the mesodorsum (fig. K26b). Case-building: a variety of cases constructed, many of fine mineral particles and curved, others of neatly arranged plant fragments (fig. 26c-f). Mainly in large water bodies, including rivers and lakes. Some are capable of swimming.

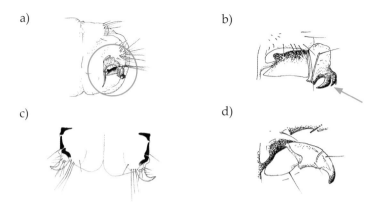

Fig. K25. Posterior of abdomen of: (a,b) Sericostomatidae: (a) lateral view, showing location of anal hook, circled; (b) anal hook, lateral view, showing accessory hooks, arrowed; (c,d) Odontoceridae: (c) dorsal view; (d) anal hook, lateral view.

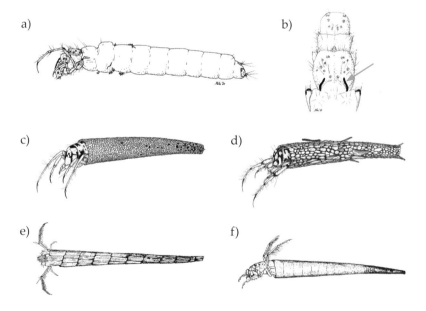

Fig. K26 Leptoceridae: (a) whole animal; (b) dorsal view of head and thorax, showing dark stripes on mesodorsum in some species (arrowed); (c-f) examples of cases.

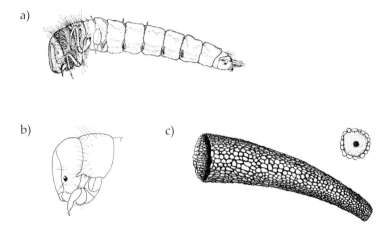

Fig. K27. Sericostomatidae: (a) whole animal; (b) *Sericostoma personatum*: anterior of animal, lateral view, with the forward-pointing corner of the prodorsum arrowed; (c) case, highlighting the small hole at the posterior end.

Table K1. Structure of cases made by case-building species.

Form of case structure	Families in which this structure is found (*families that have particularly distinctive cases)
1) Cases whose opening is not circular	
i) Square or rectangular in cross-section (rear portion of the case may be square or round); made from plant fragments or part sand grains (fig. K15c)	Brachycentridae (early instars)
	Lepidostomatidae (late instars)
ii) Two equally sized pieces, normally flattened in cross-section; made from secretions with or without small mineral or plants fragments incorporated (fig. K5b)	Hydroptilidae* (final instar, up to this point, larvae are caseless)
iii) Triangular in cross-section; made from pieces cut from dead leaves	Limnephilidae

2) Cases with a circular opening

a) Cases made from evenly-sized sand grains

i) Slightly or distinctly curved (when viewed laterally) (figs K22d, K23b, K24c, K26c, K27c)	Beraeidae
	Odontoceridae
	Sericostomatidae
	Limnephilidae
	Lepidostomatidae
	Leptoceridae
ii) Straight (when viewed laterally)	Limnephilidae
iii) Central tube with wing-like lateral projections (figs K20c, d)	Molannidae*

b) Cases made from mineral particles of different sizes or other inorganic material

i) Large particles, rounded case with equal sized openings at each end, attached to stones (figs K7c,d)	Glossosomatidae*
ii) Large particles, large opening only at the anterior end (may have some larger sand grains along the side), not attached (figs K17f, K18)	Lepidostomatidae Limnephilidae Apataniidae
iii) Small mineral particles, with a row of very large ballast stones along each side, not attached (fig. K12c)	Goeridae*
iv) Constructed from shells (fig. K17h)	Limnephilidae

c) Cases made from mineral particles and plant fragments together (figs K15d, K26d)

	Limnephilidae
	Lepidostomatidae
	Leptoceridae

d) Cases made from plant fragments

i) One or two long twigs arranged longitudinally and extending beyond the end of the case (fig. K17b)	Limnephilidae
	Leptoceridae
ii) Roughly constructed, without long twigs (figs K8c, K17e)	Limnephilidae
	Leptoceridae
	Phryganeidae
iii) Plant fragments arranged in a spiral (fig. K8d, K26e)	Leptoceridae
	Phryganeidae
iv) Elongated plant fragments arranged longitudinally and overlapping (fig. K17g)	Limnephilidae

v) Large pieces cut from dead leaves (fig. K17d)	Limnephilidae
	Phryganeidae
vi) Plant material, arranged perpendicular to the axis of the case (fig. K17c)	Limnephilidae
vii) Single piece of plant stem	Phryganeidae

e) Cases made from secretion

i) Tubular case made almost completely from secretion, with small plant fragments giving an irregular appearance, embedded sand grains, particularly in the rear half, or pieces of sponge or spicules (figs K21c, K26f)	Brachycentridae (final instar)
	Leptoceridae

Table K2. Form of structure made by caseless species
Note: apart from Psychomyiidae, structures made by caseless caddisflies are generally destroyed during sampling and so rarely seen.

Form of structure	Details	Families in which this structure is found
Galleries fixed to the surface of stones or rotting wood	Constructed from silk and debris (fig. K4b)	Psychomyiidae
Spun nets	Long, tubular bag with a very fine mesh and small mouth attached to boulders in fast-flowing water	Philopotamidae
	Nets with a coarse mesh usually built in fast-flowing water and often consisting of a simple tube, open at each end, with the front frequently extended into a wide canopy of irregular mesh (fig. K4a). The structure incorporates sand grains and other debris.	Hydropsychidae
	Nets with coarse and irregular mesh. The larvae lie in a net tube which can be broadened at each end to form uneven surfaces for prey capture.	Polycentropodidae
		Ecnomidae
No construction	(free living)	Rhyacophilidae

Key L – Coleoptera

(Beetles)

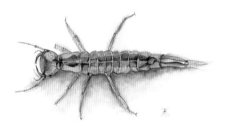

Dytiscidae larva

Dytiscidae adult

Aquatic beetles come in two distinct morphological types: adults, which are all readily identifiable as beetles, with hardened symmetrical elytra (wing cases) covering most of the thorax and abdomen; and larvae, none of which resemble adults and whose variety of forms includes those that can be confused with most other aquatic insect groups.

When identifying adult beetles, do not confuse the antennae with the maxillary palps; antennae have more segments (usually 7-11) than the maxillary palps (which appear to have three segments) (fig. L1). Sometimes only the maxillary palps are immediately obvious. Identification of preserved adults is best carried out when the specimen is dry; remove from liquid and blot dry with tissue.

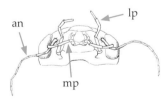

Fig. L1. Ventral view of head of adult dytiscid, with antenna, *an*, maxillary palp, *mp*, and labial palp, *lp*, arrowed.

Most aquatic beetles are found in fresh waters in both their larval and adult stages. However, a few families (Psephenidae, Scirtidae) only occur in water in the larval stage, whilst others (Helophoridae, Hyraenidae, Hydrochidae) are terrestrial as larvae and only move into water in the adult stage. Two separate keys are provided, one to adults and one to larvae; further information is provided only in the key to adults, except in the case of the families which are only aquatic as larvae.

In addition to the families covered here, there are four semi-aquatic families of very small beetles that are associated with moist habitats close to the water's edge. Limnichidae (1 species: *Limnichius pygmaeus*, 1.5-1.8 mm), Georissidae (1 species: *Georissus crenulatus*, 1-2 mm), Sphaeriusidae (1 species: *Sphaerius acaroides*, 0.5-1.2 mm) and Heteroceridae (8 species in 2 genera, 2.5-5.9 mm).

Mention must also be made of larvae of Curculionidae. This beetle family is included in the Diptera key (Key M), rather than here, because the larvae are legless; the adults appear in the adult beetle key below.

Key to adult beetles

1   Antennae long and thread-like (figs L2a & L3)—   **2**

—   Antennae normally short, segments often wider than long (fig. L2b); if antennae long, then club-like, with distinctly larger segments at the end (e.g. fig. L10b)—   **8**

Fig. L2. Dorsal views of heads, showing: (a) long antennae; (b) short antennae.

2   Front of head with a protuberance (the rostrum) to which the antennae are attached (fig. L3a)—   **Curculionidae (weevils)**

Up to 8 mm. 24 genera; 57 species. Found on leaves and stems of aquatic plants.

—   Antennae attached directly to head (figs L2a, L3b)—   **3**

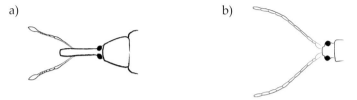

Fig. L3. Dorsal views of heads of beetles with long antennae: (a) attached to rostrum; (b) attached to head.

3   Tarsi of hind legs with four segments (fig. L4a); antennae clearly longer than head and thorax combined—   **Chrysomelidae**

Up to 13 mm long. 4 genera; 22 species. Found on leaves and stems of aquatic plants.

—   Tarsi of hind legs with five segments (fig. L4b); antennae normally shorter than combined length of head and thorax—   **4**

Fig. L4. Hind tarsi showing segmentation, with segments numbered: (a) four segments; (b) five segments.

4   Final segment of hind tarsus approximately equal to combined length of the other four segments, and widening towards its tip (fig. L5a)—
Elmidae (riffle beetles)

Up to 4.8 mm long. 8 genera; 12 species. Streams, lakes, occasionally larger rivers. Referred to as Elminthidae (and occasionally Helmidae) in some older guides.

—   Final segment of hind tarsus considerably shorter than combined length of the other four segments, and tapering towards its tip (fig. L5b)—   **5**

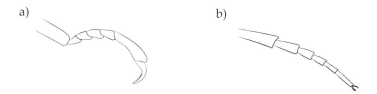

a)   b)

Fig. L5. Hind tarsi of: (a) Elmidae; (b) Haliplidae.

5   Hind coxae (leg segments closest to the body) modified into flattened plates which cover much of the abdomen and half of the femur of each hind leg (fig. L6a)—   **Haliplidae**

Up to 5 mm long. 3 genera; 19 species. Ponds, wetlands, streams, wave-washed and vegetated lake margins; also brackish ponds.

—   Hind coxae not as above (fig. L6b)—   **6**

a)   b)

Fig. L6. Ventral view of abdomen highlighting coxae: (a) Haliplidae; (b) Noteridae.

6   Back of head clearly narrower than the front of the pronotum
(fig. L7a)— **Hygrobiidae**

Up to 10 mm long. 1 species: Hygrobia hermanni. Squeaks when alarmed. This
family is occasionally referred to as Paelobiidae. Ponds.

—   Back of head similar in width to the front of the pronotum (fig. L7b)— **7**

Fig. L7. Head and pronotum in dorsal view of: (a) Hygrobiidae; (b) Dytiscidae.
Pronotum is arrowed.

7   Coxae of hind legs broad, with more or less straight outer edges; hind
margin W-shaped (figs L6b & L8a)— **Noteridae**

Up to 5 mm long. 1 genus: *Noterus*; 2 species. Ponds and fens.

—   Coxae of hind legs narrow, with curved or angled outer edges
(fig. L8b)— **Dytiscidae (diving beetles)**

Up to 38 mm long. 29 genera; 119 species. Streams, river margins, ponds,
wetlands, vegetated lake margins; also brackish ponds.

Fig. L8. Hind coxae of: (a) Noteridae; (b) Dytiscidae; outer edge arrowed.
See Fig. L6 for location of hind coxae.

8(1) Four eyes present (two above for aerial vision, two below for aquatic vision); second and third legs shorter and often wider than first legs (fig. L9a)—**Gyrinidae (whirligig beetles)**

Up to 7.8 mm long. 2 genera; 12 species. Ponds, wave-washed and vegetated lake edges, occasionally river margins; also brackish ponds. Adults often congregate at the water surface and swim round rapidly in circles.

— Clearly only two eyes; second and third legs similar in length to first legs—**9**

9 Dorsal surface covered with hairs; antennae with a distinct swelling on second segment (fig. L9b)—**Dryopidae**

Up to 5.5 mm long. 2 genera; 9 species. Streams, river margins, often associated with mud.

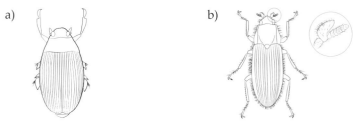

Fig. L9. Examples of adults, in dorsal view, from families: (a) Gyrinidae; (b) Dryopidae with antenna circled.

— Dorsal surface not hairy and without swelling on second segment of antennae—**5 families, Table L1 (fig. L10)**

Spercheidae – Up to 7 mm long. 1 species: *Spercheus emarginatus*, probably extinct in Britain and never recorded from Ireland. Considered by some to be a subfamily of Hydrophilidae.
Hydrophilidae – Up to 48 mm long. 17 genera; 70 species. Ponds, wetlands, occasionally streams; also brackish ponds; river margins.
Hydrochidae - Up to 4.5 mm long. 1 genus, *Hydrochus*; 7 species. Standing and running waters.
Hydraenidae - Up to 2.5 mm long. 4 genera; 32 species. Streams, ponds, wetlands; also brackish ponds.
Helophoridae - Up to 7.5 mm long. 1 genus: *Helophorus*; 20 species. Standing waters.

KEY L – COLEOPTERA

Table L1. Beetles distinguished by antennae that are club-like (fig. L10b) and, except for some Hydrophilidae, maxillary palps that are longer than antennae. Families marked * were formerly clumped together as Hydrophilidae.

Family	Widest point of pronotum	Size range (mm)	Distinguishing feature/s
Hydraenidae (*Limnebius*)	Towards rear (fig. L10a)	1 - 2.5	Wing cases with truncate (straight) rear end (fig. L10a)
Hydrophilidae *	Towards rear or rear edge (fig. L10b)	1 - 48+	Wing cases with curved rear end
Hydraenidae (excl. *Limnebius*)	Towards centre	1 - 2.5	Pronotum either with two longitudinal shallow depressions; two transverse shallow pits or a longitudinal groove down the middle
Spercheidae *	Towards centre	5.5 - 7	Front margin of head slightly concave; pronotum with two shallow depressions
Helophoridae *	Towards front	2 - 7.5	Five longitudinal grooves on pronotum (fig. L10c)
Hydrochidae *	Towards front	2 - 4.5	Pronotum with five rounded depressions (fig. L10d); wing cases and underside with punctures

+Only two species are greater than 10mm.

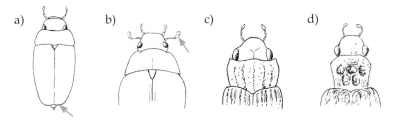

Fig. L10. Examples of adults, in dorsal view, from families: (a) Hydraenidae, *Limnebius* type showing truncate end of wing cases (arrowed); (b) Hydrophilidae, showing club-shaped antennae (arrowed); (c) Helophoridae; (d) Hydrochidae.

Key to beetle larvae

Note: All larvae are shown in dorsal view unless otherwise stated. Several end points in the key refer to types (e.g. *Peltodytes*-type); these give the name of a typical genus that looks like this type, but do not definitively identify the specimen as that genus.

1   Animal grub-like, with legs reduced and fleshy prothorax several times longer than head (fig. L12e)— **Chrysomelidae**

—   Not as above; legs usually prominent; head distinct— **2**

2   Legs with four segments and a single claw (fig. L11a); no abdominal gills— **3**

—   Legs with five segments and a double claw (fig. L11b) (although second claw very small in family Haliplidae, fig.L13a); abdominal gills may be present— **7**

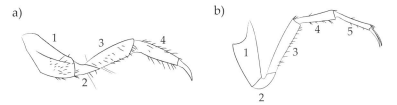

a)   b)

Fig. L11. Legs with segments numbered: (a) Scirtidae; (b) Dytiscidae.

Note: This next 'couplet' has three end points.

3   Eight abdominal segments (therefore 11 body segments plus the head) (fig. L12a, b)— **4**

—   Nine abdominal segments (therefore 12 body segments plus the head) (fig. L12c, d)— **5**

—   Ten abdominal segments (therefore 13 body segments plus the head)— **Spercheidae**

Most abdominal segments have a pair of small lateral gills.

4   Antennae long (fig. L12a)—   **Scirtidae**

Up to 8 mm long (larval length: only found in fresh water as larvae). 7 genera;
20 species. Streams, ponds, wetlands. Referred to as Helodidae in some older
guides.

—   Antennae short (fig. L12b)—   **Hydrophilidae**

5(3) Head visible when viewed from above—   **6**

—   Head hidden when viewed from above—   **Psephenidae (water penny)**

Up to 4 mm long. 1 species: *Eubria palustris*. Cling to the underside of stones or
sticks in streams.

6   Body covered with wart-like small protuberances; hairy tufts present at
       the end of the abdomen (fig. L12c)—   **Elmidae**

—   Body generally smooth; no hairy tufts on the abdomen (fig. L12d)—
                                                            Dryopidae

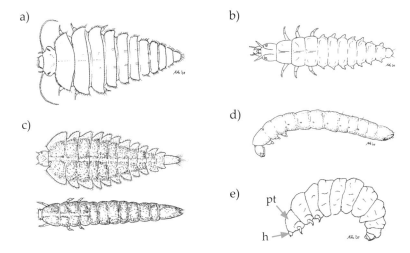

Fig. L12. Coleoptera larvae with four leg segments: (a) Scirtidae;
(b) Hydrophilidae; (c) Elmidae - *Elmis* type (top) and *Limnius* type (bottom);
(d) Dryopidae (lateral view); (e) Chrysomelidae (lateral view) with prothorax, *pt*,
and head, *h*, arrowed.

7(2) Gills present on abdomen (fig. L14a-c)—   **8**

—   No abdominal gills (fig. L14d-f)—   **10**

8   Only ventral gills present (fig. L14a)—
                                        Hygrobiidae, *Hygrobia hermanni*

—   Gills dorsal and/or lateral—   **9**

9   Lateral abdominal gills (fig. L14b); four hooks at end of abdomen—
                                                          Gyrinidae

—   Dorsal and lateral gills on thorax and abdomen (fig. L14c); no hooks at
       end of abdomen—   **Haliplidae - part:** *Peltodytes* **type**

10(7) Single large claw, the second claw vestigial (fig. L13a)—
                              Haliplidae - part: *Haliplus* **type** (fig. L14d)

—   Clear double claw (fig. L13b)—   **11**

11   Long pincer-like jaws (fig. L15a) that normally stick out in front of head
       (fig. L14e)—   **Dytiscidae**

—   Jaws not pincer-like (fig. L15b) and not protruding beyond the front of
       the head (fig. L14f)—   **Noteridae**

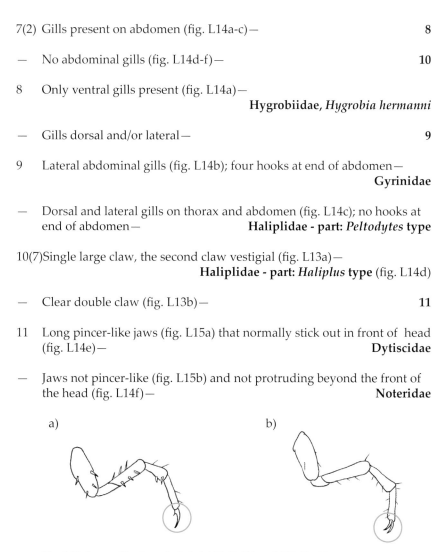

Fig. L13. Legs with claw circled: (a) Haliplidae; (b) Dytiscidae.

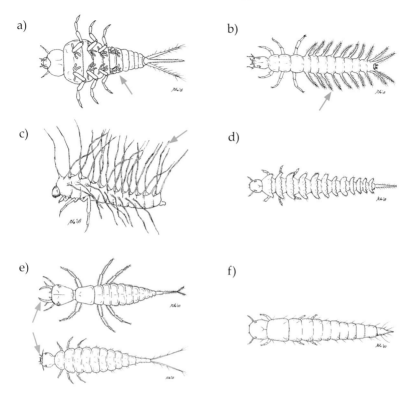

Fig. L14. Coleoptera larvae with five leg segments: (a) Hygrobiidae (ventral view with gill arrowed); (b) Gyrinidae (with lateral abdominal gill arrowed); (c) Haliplidae, *Peltodytes* type (lateral view with abdominal gill arrowed); (d) Haliplidae, *Haliplus* type; (e) Dytiscidae with jaws arrowed: *Dytiscus* type (top) and *Agabus* type (bottom); (f) Noteridae.

Fig. L15. Jaws of: (a) Dytiscidae; (b) Noteridae.

147

Key M – Diptera

(True Flies)

Chaoboridae sp.

True fly larvae are very diverse and abundant in most fresh waters, and can cause problems with identification as all are worm-like or maggot-like, and some lack even an obvious head capsule. Their identification uses a variety of morphological features. Major ones include the presence or otherwise of an obvious head capsule; the presence, number and location of prolegs; and the structure of the final abdominal segment and any respiratory features associated with it.

An identification feature for many Diptera larvae is the posterior spiracles, respiratory openings on the final abdominal segment. These are often very distinct as a pair of darkened circles or ovals (e.g. figs M25b and M27c), or as darkened tips to abdominal extensions (e.g. figs M41 and M42), and the structure of this segment, including location of spiracles and of lobes or other extensions, is diagnostically important. Some Diptera larvae also appear hairy. True hairs occur only in mammals and these structures are more properly known as setae, but the term 'hairy' has been used at several places in this key as it conveys the overall impression of the feature.

As some Diptera pupae are relatively active, a key to Diptera pupae is also provided. The larva of the beetle family Curculionidae (weevils) is included here in the larval key, as it is legless; it is not commonly encountered, as it lives within the leaves of aquatic plants.

Aquatic or semi-aquatic habits are found in a large number of Diptera families. The habitats occupied by some species include damp soil, moist rotting vegetation and other waterlogged environments, blurring the boundaries between aquatic and terrestrial species, whilst others specialise in water-filled tree holes. Therefore, this key includes some forms which are very unlikely to occur in rivers, lakes or ponds. In addition to the families that are keyed out here, there are several families recorded from Britain and Ireland as terrestrial species that may turn up in British fresh waters in due course: Lonchopteridae, Scatopsidae and Bibionidae; all have recently been recorded from peripheral aquatic habitats elsewhere in western Europe. Lonchopteridae have seven visible body segments, each of which has a sclerotised dorsal plate; Scatopsidae has a hardened head capsule and with two posterior spiracles, each on the end of a short cylindrical tube; Bibionidae has a hardened head capsule and a pair of spiracles on each body segment.

Among some families, the number of aquatic species is unknown, as the larvae have not yet been described. Therefore, some of the estimates of species richness may include species that in reality have terrestrial larvae, a situation compounded by the number of species in some families that occupy peripheral habitats.

Key to Diptera larvae

Note: In all figures of whole animals, the anterior end (head) end is towards the left and the animal is shown in lateral (side) view unless otherwise stated.

1   Distinct, hard head capsule present, not retractable into the soft body (the head may be very small) —   **2**

—   No obvious head capsule, or head retractable into soft body —   **30**

2   With wing cases enveloping the front of the body (fig. M1), along with jointed legs fixed to the surface of the thorax (e.g. figs M44, M47)—

Key to Diptera pupae (page 173)

a)   th   b)

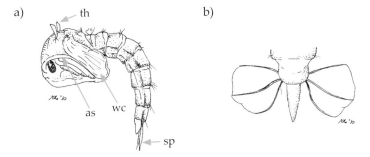

Fig. M1. (a) Culicidae pupa, with wing case, *wc*, antenna sheath, *as*, thoracic horn, *th*, and swimming paddle, *sp*, arrowed. (b) Chaoboridae pupa: dorsal view of end of abdomen, showing paddles.

—   No wings or jointed legs (although prolegs may be present)—   **3**

3   Body segments clearly swollen, giving the animal a squat appearance; prolegs absent (fig. M2)—   **Order COLEOPTERA: Curculionidae**

See Key L for more details.

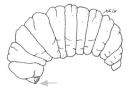

Fig. M2. Curculionidae, with head arrowed.

—   Body appearance slender; if any clear swelling, it is towards the front of the body; prolegs often present—   **4**

4   Ventral prolegs present (at the front and/or rear of the body or at the
     front of the abdomen e.g. figs M3, M4)—   **5**

—   Prolegs absent—   **14**

5   Spiny protuberances present on thorax and abdomen (fig. M3)—
                                    Ceratopogonidae – part: Forcipomyinae

     Up to 5 mm long. 2 genera; 24 species. Marginally aquatic: damp soil at
     the water's edge. If there are lateral projections as well as dorsal ones, it is
     Atrichopogon; if there are only dorsal projections it is *Forcipomyia*.

Fig. M3. *Atrichopogon* (Ceratopogonidae: Forcipomyinae), with proleg, *p*,
arrowed.

—   No spiny protuberances—   **6**

6   Distinct swelling of the rear half of the abdomen; basal pad of abdomen
     with many small hooks in a circular formation; a single fused proleg at
     the front only (fig. M4)—   **Simuliidae (blackflies)**

     Up to 10 mm long. 3 genera; 33 species. All species aquatic. Filter feeders in
     fast-flowing waters, where they cling on to a firm surface using their abdominal
     hooks and catch particles with their fan-like modified antennae. Adults are
     blood suckers (and some species attack humans).

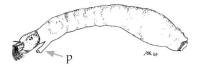

Fig. M4. Simuliidae, with fused anterior proleg, *p*, arrowed.

—   Base of abdomen no wider than thorax and lacking a circle of hooks—
                                                                                7

7   Prolegs on the front two abdominal segments; often bent into a U-shape
(fig. M5) —   **Dixidae (meniscus midges)**

Up to 8 mm long. 2 genera; 15 species. All species aquatic. Surface film amongst
emergent vegetation. *Dixa* has a distinct crown of setae on the dorsal surface of
5-6 abdominal segments (fig. M5a) and is found mainly in stream pools; *Dixella*
has no such features and is typically found in ponds.

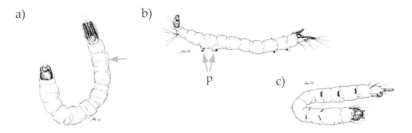

Fig. M5. Dixidae: (a) *Dixa*, dorsal view showing crown of setae, arrowed;
b-c *Dixella*, (b) lateral view, showing prolegs, *p*, arrowed; (c) ventral view.

—   Prolegs on thorax and/or posterior end of abdomen, but not at the front
of the abdomen —   **8**

8   Prolegs present only at the rear of the abdomen (fig. M6) —
                         Ceratopogonidae – part: Dasyheleinae

Up to 10 mm long. 1 genus: *Dasyhelea*; 11 species. Marginally aquatic. The
prolegs are retractable into a tube.

Fig. M6. *Dasyhelea* (Ceratopogonidae: Dasyheleinae), with proleg, *p*, arrowed.

—   Prolegs both on the first segment of the thorax and at the rear of the
abdomen —   **9**

9   Spiracles on first thoracic segment (fig. M7a) and on dorsal side of last abdominal segment; anterior prolegs fused —

Thaumaleidae (fig. M7)

Up to 15 mm long. 1 genus: *Thaumalea*; 3 species. Small bumps present on front of head (fig. M7a). All species aquatic. Very shallow water running over rock surfaces.

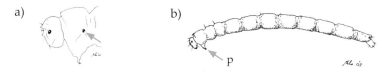

a)   b)

Fig. M7. Thaumaleidae: *Thaumalea*: (a) spiracle on first thoracic segment arrowed; (b) whole animal, with proleg, *p*, arrowed.

—   No spiracles on thorax; anterior prolegs separate, although they may appear fused towards the base — **Chironomidae** (fig. M8): **10**

Up to 20 mm long. 139 genera; around 500 species. Non-biting midges. Almost all species aquatic: every type of freshwater and brackish habitat, including species adapted to living in grossly polluted water, plus a few species living in salt water. Several subfamilies can be distinguished. The subfamily Telmatogetoninae, which is similar to Orthocladiinae, is not keyed out here; it has two marine species which live on intertidal rocks.

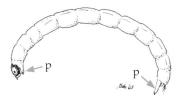

Fig. M8. Chironomidae: Orthocladiinae, showing prolegs, *p*, arrowed.

10 Antennae retractable into head capsule (antennae stick out forwards beyond the front of the head, rather than sideways (fig. M9a)); a single eye on each side— **Tanypodinae**

Head normally wider than thorax, and uniformly yellow or golden brown in colour. Eye usually kidney shaped.

— Antennae not retractable (stick out sideways or at a clear angle to the head (fig. M9b-c); normally two eyes on each side— **11**

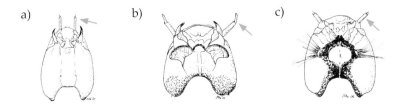

Fig. M9. Chironomidae, ventral view of head: (a) Tanypodinae; (b) Chironomini; (c) Prodiamesinae. Arrows point to antennae.

11 Procercus (dorsal extension on the final abdominal segment) at least eight times as long as wide— **Podonominae**

Cold springs and streams.

— Procercus no more than four times as long as wide (fig. M10b)— **12**

Fig. M10. Orthocladiinae: (a) lateral view of head, showing occipital band, arrowed; (b) posterior end with procercus, arrowed.

12   Two eyes on each side, situated one above the other (fig. M11a) —
                                                                    Chironominae

Often bright red in life. There are two distinctive tribes. The Tanytarsini have
antennae that are usually longer than half the length of the head and attached to
the head on an elongated pedestal (fig. M11a); the Chironomini have antennae
that are less than half the length of the head, and attached directly to the head,
or on a short pedestal. The Chironomini also have a pair of small but distinctive
semi-circular plates, often striped like a fan, on the underside of the head
(fig. M9b).

Fig. M11. Chironomid heads in lateral view: (a) Chironominae (Tanytarsini);
(b) Diamesinae, with occipital band, arrowed.

—   Either one eye on each side or, if two, situated one in front of the
      other —   **13**

13   Underside of head has distinctive whiskers (fig. M9c); eyes placed
      obliquely relative to each other —   **Prodiamesinae**

—   Underside of head lacks whiskers —
                              Orthocladiinae (fig. M8) **and Diamesinae**

These subfamilies are separable by the structure of the antennae, which have
annulations (rings) in Diamesinae. This feature is, however, very difficult
to see without high magnification. A less definitive method is to look at the
occipital band around the rear of the head; in Diamesinae, this is generally
dark and distinct (fig. M11b), whereas in Orthocladiinae it tends to be less
obvious (fig. M10a). Diamesinae occur mainly in cold springs and streams;
Orthocladiinae are widespread in most aquatic habitats.

14(4) Thorax clearly swollen relative to abdomen— **15**

— Thorax not swollen relative to abdomen— **21**

15   Antennae jointed and ending in stout setae at least as long as the final antennal segment (fig. M12a); very pale or transparent (although preserved specimens may become opaque) (fig. M12b)—
Chaoboridae (phantom midges)

Up to 12 mm long. 2 genera; 6 species. All species aquatic. Swimming larvae, in ponds, lakes and marshes. *Chaoborus* has a distinctive oval or sausage-shaped feature visible within its first thoracic segment – an air sac to help it float; it also has a smaller one towards the back of the abdomen. *Mochlonyx* lacks the obvious air sac at the front but has a cylindrical respiratory siphon on the dorsal side of the last abdominal segment. The only Diptera larvae that can be regularly found in larger lakes away from the safety of fringing vegetation.

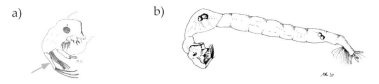

Fig. M12. Chaoboridae: *Chaoborus*: (a) detail of head with final antennal segment arrowed; (b) whole animal.

— Antennae without joints and with setae considerably shorter than final antennal segment (fig. M13b)— **Culicidae (mosquitoes): 16**

Up to 12 mm long. 8 genera; 34 species. All species aquatic. Small still water bodies of all types. Common in temporary water bodies and in small artificial features such as drinking troughs and water butts. Some British species readily bite humans, particularly in the genus *Anopheles*.

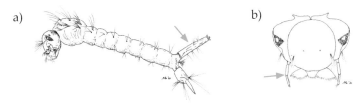

Fig. M13. Culicidae: (a) *Culex*, whole animal with dorsal siphon arrowed; (b) *Culiseta*, detail of head in dorsal view with antenna arrowed.

16   Dorsal siphon present at end of abdomen (fig. M13a) —   **Culicinae: 17**

—   Dorsal siphon absent but a pair of dorsal spiracles present — **Anophelinae**

      One genus: *Anopheles*.

17   Dorsal siphon short (length < 2x width) with a pointed end —
                                                    Coquillettidia richiardii

—   Dorsal siphon longer (length > 2x width), slightly tapering but not
      pointed —   **18**

18   Pecten (row of spines or setae) present on each side of the dorsal siphon
      (fig. M14) —   **19**

—   No pecten present; found in tree holes —   *Orthopodomyia pulcripalpis*

19   Three or more pairs of tufts of setae on the dorsal siphon (fig. M14a) —
                                                    Culex (fig. M13a)

—   Only one pair of tufts of setae on the dorsal siphon (fig. M14b) —   **20**

20   Tufts of setae inserted at the base of the dorsal siphon (fig. M14b) —
                                                    Culiseta

      Species of *Culiseta* in the subgenus *Culiseta* have a pecten consisting of long hair-
      like structures (fig. M14b). Among other species, if the respiratory siphon is less
      than three times as long as wide, then it is the very rare subgenus *Allotheobaldia*;
      if more than four times as long as wide it is the subgenus *Culicella*.

—   Tufts of setae inserted half way along the dorsal siphon —
                              Aedes **group (***Aedes, Dahlaia* **and** *Ochlerotatus***)**

      These genera were all formerly included under *Aedes* as subgenera; *Dahlaia* is the
      name given to species formerly included in the subgenus *Finlaya*.

a)   p

b)   p

Fig. M14. Culicidae posterior end: (a) *Culex* showing spiny pecten, *p*, plus three tufts of setae; (b) *Culiseta* showing hair-like pecten, *p*, plus one tuft of setae.

21(14) Posterior end with a long tapering siphon, often at least half as long as the rest of the body, often with two small papillae visible at its base —
Ptychopteridae (phantom craneflies) (fig. M15)

Up to 35 mm long. 1 genus: *Ptychoptera*; 7 species. All species aquatic. Shallow, muddy-bottomed or detritus-filled water.

Fig. M15. Ptychopteridae: *Ptychoptera*.

— No long siphon — **22**

22 Body smooth, very slender and cylindrical in cross section —
Ceratopogonidae – part: Ceratopogoninae (fig. M16)

Up to 15 mm long. 17 genera; 111 species. Peripherally aquatic, in wet meadows, ditches and shallow marshes, but occasionally in streams. Includes the genus *Culicoides*, the infamous biting midges of the Scottish highlands and other upland areas.

Fig. M16. Ceratopogonidae: Ceratopogoninae.

— Body textured or with hardened plates, flattened in cross section — **23**

23 Dorsal surface with numerous transverse sclerotised plates
(figs M17, M18) and/or lateral fringes of setae; mouthparts opposable
mandibles — **Psychodidae (moth flies or owl midges): 24**

Up to 30 mm long, but most less than half this length. 21 genera; 92 species.
Most are very dark in appearance. Marginally aquatic, in vegetation and detritus
at the edge of ponds and streams.

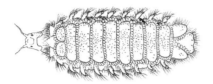

Fig. M17. Psychodidae: *Sycorax* (Sycoracinae), dorsal view.

Fig. M18. Psychodidae: Pericomini (Psychodinae): (a) whole animal, dorsal view;
(b) posterior end, in lateral view, showing latero-anal plate, *lap*, and dorsal
plate, *dp*.

— Dorsal surface roughened and patterned (fig. M19); mouthparts parallel
hooks— **Stratiomyidae (soldierflies): 26**

Up to 55 mm long, although most are considerably shorter. 7 aquatic genera;
39 species. A family with clearly aquatic and clearly terrestrial species (the latter
not keyed out here), with only one genus (*Beris*) found in marginal habitats.

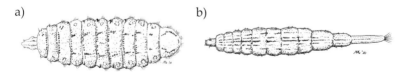

Fig. M19. Stratiomyidae: (a) *Beris* (Beridinae), dorsal view; (b) *Stratiomys*
(Stratiomyidae), dorsal view.

24 Body somewhat oval in shape, with no subdivision of segments and no dorsal sclerotised plates— **Sycoracinae** (fig. M17)

  1 genus: *Sycorax*, 3 species. In moss at the edge of streams. The only psychodid with distinct antennae.

— Body more elongate, with subdivision so it appears to have more than 13 segments, and with hardened plates on the dorsal surface of at least some segments— **Psychodinae: 25**

25 Dorsal hardened plates on only on rear subdivisions of the body— **Psychodini**

  Sometimes referred to as *'Psychoda*-type.

— Dorsal hardened plates on almost every subdivision of the body— **Pericomini** (fig. M18a) **and Telmatoscopini**

  Distinguishable by the presence (Pericomini) or absence (Telmatoscopini) of latero-anal plates (fig. M18b), but these are small and often difficult to see, so they are sometimes lumped together as *'Pericoma*-type'.

26(23) Posterior end rounded; no distinctive tuft of setae but clearly very hairy in appearance— **Beridinae:** *Beris* (fig. M19a)

  Marginally aquatic, in wet moss and decaying vegetation at the edge of streams.

— Posterior end not as above— **27**

27 Antennae situated near the middle of the head, so the front of the head extends clearly beyond the end of the antenna (fig. M20a); up to 10 mm long— **Clitellarinae: 28**

— Antennae situated near the front of the head, so the end of the antenna reaches or extends beyond the head (fig. M20b); up to 55 mm long— **Stratiomyinae: 29**

Fig. M20. Stratiomyidae heads in dorsal view, with antennae arrowed:
(a) *Oxycera* (Clitellarinae); (b) *Odontomyia* (Stratiomyinae).

28   Posterior end with few setae but distinctly concave (fig. M21)—
Nemotelus

Mud in marshes.

—   Posterior end with a distinctive tuft or coronet of setae—
Oxycera (figs M20a, M22) **and Vanoya**

Wet mosses in marshes and on sloping rock faces.

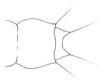

Fig. M21. Stratiomyidae: *Nemotelus* (Clitellarinae) posterior end, dorsal view.

Fig. M22. Stratiomyidae: *Oxycera* (Stratiomyinae), dorsal view.

29(27) Posterior segment very long and slender, at least 4x longer than wide; anal slit situated near the base of the anal segment and with a prominent swelling (fig. M23a); ventral hooks absent—

Stratiomys (fig. M19b)

Very shallow standing water.

— Length of posterior segment no more than 3x its width (fig. M23b) or, if longer, ventral hooks present on rear abdominal segments (fig. M23c); anus situated towards the middle of the anal segment, and not on a prominent swelling— *Odontomyia* (fig. M20b) **and** *Oplodontha*

Very shallow standing water.

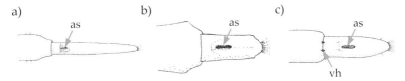

Fig. M23. Stratiomyinae (posterior end, ventral view): (a) *Stratiomys*; (b) *Odontomyia*, without ventral hooks; (c) *Odontomyia*, with ventral hooks. Anal slit, *as*, and ventral hook, *vh*, arrowed.

30(1) Mandibles horizontal and act as pincers; head capsule entirely hardened— **31**

Note: the mandibles may be completely withdrawn into the head and therefore invisible. Look at the front of the thorax where there will be a groove into which the head is withdrawn: if this groove is horizontally orientated, then the mandibles are also going to be horizontal.

The four families with horizontal mandibles (Cylindrotomidae, Limoniidae, Pediciidae, Tipulidae), collectively known as craneflies, were formerly all included in the Tipulidae, either as subfamilies (e.g. Cylindrotominae) or tribes (e.g. Pediciini).

— Mandibles vertical and parallel, often hook-like, or no obvious mouthparts; head capsule either entirely or partially hardened, or apparently absent— **34**

31 Prominent soft extensions, arranged in longitudinal lines, all along the body— **Cylindrotomidae** (fig. M24)

Up to 30 mm long. 2 aquatic genera; 2 species. Found in mosses and easily overlooked. If the growths on its back are toothed, then it is *Triogma distinctissima*. If the growths are elongated, maybe branching into two but otherwise smooth, then it is *Phalacrocera replicata*. Also one terrestrial genus.

Fig. M24. Cylindrotomidae: *Phalacrocera replicata*.

— Extensions confined to lobes at the posterior end of the abdomen— **32**

32 Posterior end of abdomen with six lobes around the spiracular disc (do not confuse lobes around the spiracles with anal papillae, which extend from underneath the spiracular disc. See fig. M25b)— **Tipulidae** (fig. M25a)

Up to 60 mm long. 5 aquatic genera; 45 species. Prolegs never present. Most species terrestrial, occurring in soil, but some species in decaying vegetation in fresh water, particularly lake edges, wetlands and streams.

a)   b)

Fig. M25. Tipulidae: *Tipula*: (a) whole animal; (b) posterior end with spiracles, *s*, lobes, *l*, and anal papillae, *ap*, arrowed.

— Posterior end of abdomen with five or fewer lobes around the spiracular disc— **33**

33 Two lobes present on the ventral side of the spiracular disc
(fig. M26b)—   **Pediciidae** (fig. M26)

Up to 50 mm long. 3 aquatic genera; 17 species. Pools and shallow trickles, and occasionally in larger water bodies, including streams. Two common genera: *Dicranota* has five pairs of well-developed prolegs (see fig. M26b), each with a prominent circular row of small hooks on the tip; *Pedicia* has four pairs of welts or short prolegs (fig. M26a), without rows of hooks. Also one terrestrial genus.

One genus of Limoniidae, *Antocha*, will key out here. It has only two lobes, but is distinguishable from Pediciidae by the absence of posterior spiracles and by the presence of distinct welts on both the dorsal and ventral sides of abdominal segments 2-7. It lives in tubes in running waters.

Fig. M26. Pediciidae: (a) *Pedicia*, whole animal; (b) *Dicranota*, posterior end with lobes arrowed.

— Four or five spiracular lobes present, or lobes absent—
                                              Limoniidae (fig. M27)

Up to 20 mm long. 49 genera; over 200 species; the number of genera and species that are aquatic or semi-aquatic is unknown. Mostly in peripheral habitats, occasionally straying into water. Very variable but never with prolegs. Often covered with fine downy setae (figs M27a-c), and the rear end has a distinctive tuft of setae in some genera (fig. M27d). Occasionally specimens are found with a swollen rear segment, but this is not a diagnostic feature.

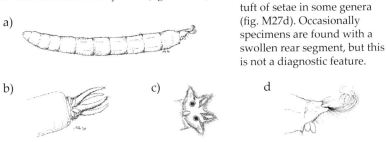

Fig. M27. Limoniidae: (a) whole animal; (b-d) examples of posterior end of some distinctive genera (b) *Eloeophila*, ventral view showing four spiracular lobes; (c) *Helius*, dorsal view showing five spiracular lobes; (d) *Neolimnomyia*, lateral view showing distinct tufts of long setae on spiracular lobes.

34(30) Rear spiracles on a single posterior extension —   **35**

—   Spiracles either not on extensions, or on a pair of clearly separate appendages —   **41**

35   Posterior extension either long (at least ¼ body length and often many times this) and flexible or short and needle-like (figs M28, M29); prolegs may be present —   **Syrphidae (hoverflies): 36**

Up to 20 mm long, not including the siphon which can extend in some species to several times this length. 17 aquatic genera; around 50 species. Most are terrestrial and some live in rot holes in trees. Aquatic species generally in standing waters with plenty of decaying vegetation, and some are found in wet manure and even liquefied decaying flesh. Adults are familiar as hoverflies. The family is commonly divided into tribes; although these are not universally recognised, they are useful for further subdivision of larvae and so are included here.

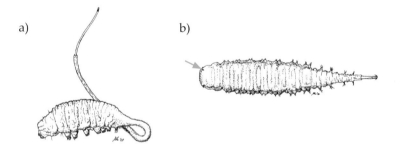

a)   b)

Fig. M28. Syrphidae: a) Eristalini; b) Sphegina (Spheginini); arrow points to anterior spiracle.

—   A single squat appendage on the dorsal side of the last abdominal segment, plus a V-shaped ridge around the anal area; prolegs absent, but distinct welts form rings encircling each abdominal segment (fig. M31) —   **Tabanidae (horseflies): 39**

Up to 40 mm long, although most are smaller than 25 mm. 5 aquatic genera; 29 species. Peripherally aquatic, in small trickles and the edges of streams.

36   Abdomen abruptly tapers to a long tail with a telescopic breathing tube;
      prolegs present—
                        Eristalini (fig. M28) **and Sericomyiini (rat-tailed maggots)**

Most species that key out here will belong to the tribe Eristalini. The tribe
Sericomyiini has one truly aquatic genus, *Sericomyia*, which lives in pools in peat
bogs, plus *Arctophila*, which is marginally aquatic.

—   Abdomen either with a short tail or gradually tapering; prolegs present
      or absent—   **37**

37   Anterior spiracles absent or small and indistinct; end of abdomen forms
      a clear tail or a distinct needle-like structure—
                                            Chrysogasterini - part (fig. M29)

Includes *Melanogaster hirtella*, which has a distinctive needle-like end (fig. M29b),
which it uses to pierce aquatic plant stems to obtain oxygen.

a)   b)

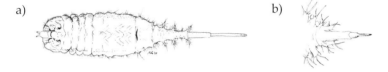

Fig. M29. Syrphidae (Chrysogasterini): (a) *Chrysogaster*, whole animal, ventral
view; (b) *Melanogaster hirtella*, posterior end, ventral view.

—   Anterior spiracles clearly distinct as small protrusions on the dorsal side
      of the thorax (fig. M30; see also fig. M28b); end of abdomen gradually
      tapers or forms a distinct tail—   **38**

38   A pair of large dorsal hooks on the front of the thorax—
                              Chrysogasterini - part: *Neoascia* (fig. M30a)

Mainly associated with farmyard manure, but occurs in swampy vegetation.

—   No large hooks on the front of the thorax, although there are small
      hooks (spicules) on the prothorax (fig. M30b)—   **Spheginini:** *Sphegina*

Associated with wet bark, so occasionally in submerged wood.

Fig. M30. Syrphidae: (a) *Neoascia* (Chrysogasterini), anterior end, with pair of large hooks, *h*, and anterior spiracles, *as*, arrowed; (b) *Sphegina* (Spheginini), anterior end, with a large numbers of spicules, *sp*, and anterior spiracles, *as*, arrowed.

39(35) Four widely spaced lateral and ventral welts on each abdominal segment (fig. M32a) — **Chrysopsinae: *Chrysops***

— Six lateral and ventral welts on each abdominal segment, of which four are in closely adjacent pairs (fig. M32b) — **Tabaninae: 40**

40 Posterior segment higher than it is long (fig. M33a) — **Haematopotini: *Haematopota***

Occasionally in marshy soil, but not really aquatic.

— Posterior segment longer than high (fig. M33b) — **Tabanini** (fig. M31)

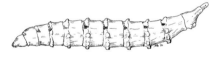

Fig. M31. Tabanidae: *Tabanus* (Tabanini).

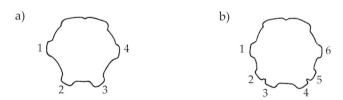

Fig. M32. Tabanidae: cross section through (a) *Chrysops* (Chrysopsinae); (b) Tabaninae, showing lateral and ventral welts (numbered).

a)

b)

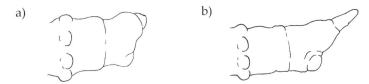

Fig. M33. Tabanidae: posterior end of (a) *Haematopota* (Haematopotini); (b) Tabanini.

41(34) Prolegs present on ventral side—   **42**

—   Prolegs absent, although hardened welts may be present on ventral side or encircling segments—   **44**

42   Either two flattened, distinctly hairy appendages on last abdominal segments or five pairs of very long, slender appendages extending beyond the rear of the abdomen—   **Athericidae** (fig. M34)

Up to 25 mm long. 3 genera; 3 species. All species aquatic. Streams. If it has just seven pairs of prolegs and five pairs of long, simple projections from the rear abdominal segments, more than a third as long as the body, then it is *Atrichops crassipes*. If it has an extra single proleg on its last abdominal segment, and only two rear projections, much shorter than the body length and quite feathery in appearance, it is one of the other two. *Atherix ibis* has short lateral abdominal projections and lives in fast-flowing water, while *Ibisia marginata* has longer projections and lives in slow-flowing water.

Fig. M34. Athericidae: dorsal-lateral view.

—   Not as above; appendages either absent or without fringes of setae—   **43**

43　A pair of long siphons present at the rear of the abdomen, often diverging from the end of a single extension—

Ephydridae - part (fig. M35)

There are two genera with prolegs: *Ephydra*, which lives in saltmarshes, and *Setacera*, a freshwater genus. Both have a distinctively large rear pair of prolegs (fig. M35).

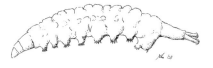

Fig. M35. Ephydridae: *Setacera*.

—　No siphons at rear end, although short lobes may be present—

Empididae (fig. M36) **and Muscidae - part**

Empididae are up to 7 mm long. 14 aquatic genera; around 70 species. Also four terrestrial genera. Rivers and streams. There are two distinctive subfamilies. Clinocerinae have eight pairs of prolegs, and often three or four lobes, in addition to prolegs, on the last abdominal segment. Hemerodrominae have seven pairs of prolegs, of which the rear pair may be relatively large; the genus *Chelifera* is distinctive as it has a rounded back end with a little tuft of setae (fig. M36).

The genus *Limnophora* (Muscidae) (fig. M41) may key out here, as it has seven pairs of welts which are often large enough to be interpreted as prolegs. It has two pairs of extensions to the last abdominal segment, of which the dorsal pair curve to face towards the anterior end and have a distinctively darker tip.

Fig. M36. Empididae: *Chelifera*.

44(41) Spiracles on the end of two lobes (which may be very short or modified into short piercing spines), the lobes either diverging from the end of a single extension or meeting at their base —
Ephydridae - part (fig. M37)

Up to 18 mm long. 10 aquatic genera; 40 species. Also many terrestrial species. Aquatic plants in wetlands and shallow pools; some species of *Notiphila* and *Hydrellia* (fig. M37a) live within plant tissue; they obtain their oxygen from plant cells and the two lobes are adapted to pierce the plant tissue.

a)   b)

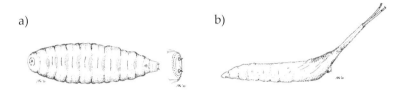

Fig. M37. Ephydridae: (a) *Hydrellia*, whole animal, ventral view and close up of rear end showing lobes modified into piercing spines; (b) *Coenia* whole animal.

— Spiracles not on lobes— **45**

45 Spiracles covered by a pair of circular features with branched filaments (fig. M38b); body heavily wrinkled, without welts—
Sciomyzidae (fig. M38)

Up to 20 mm long. 16 aquatic genera; around 50 species. Also many terrestrial species. Standing waters in association with snails, upon which they prey.

a)   b)

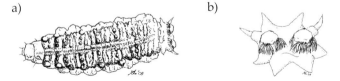

Fig. M38. Sciomyzidae: (a) whole animal, dorsal view; (b) posterior end.

— Spiracles not covered as above; welts on ventral side; end of posterior abdominal segment normally with a series of short lobes around the spiracular disc— **Dolichopodidae, Ephydridae - part, Muscidae - part, Rhagionidae and Scathophagidae**
See notes opposite

Notes on Dolichopodidae, Empididae, Ephydridae, Muscidae, Rhagionidae and Scathophagidae.

These families are distinguished by the shape of the extensions on the last segment. Dolichopodidae (fig. M39) has four lobes, the ventral lobes longer than the dorsal lobes, whereas Rhagionidae has four lobes of approximately equal size (fig. M40). Among Muscidae, *Limnophora* has four extensions that are approximately equal in length, of which the dorsal pair are respiratory siphons, with a darker tip, that characteristically bend towards the front (fig. M41); *Graphomya* has two short siphons, attached dorsally (fig. M42a); while *Lispe* has no siphons but a pair of distinct spiracles (fig. M42b).

Fig. M39. Dolichopodidae.

Fig. M40. Rhagionidae.

Fig. M41. Muscidae: *Limnophora*.

Scathophagidae have a series of very short lobes around a flat posterior end that is orientated at a slight angle relative to the plane if the body (fig. M43). If there are two spiracles on the end of a pair of long siphons, it is Ephydridae (fig. M37).

Scathophagidae are up to 10 mm long. 9 aquatic genera; 9 species. Also many terrestrial species. Peripherally aquatic, in detritus at the edge of water bodies.

Rhagionidae are up to 12 mm long. 2 peripherally aquatic genera: *Chrysophilus* and *Rhagio*: 10 species, although probably not all are aquatic. Decaying vegetation.

Muscidae are up to 16 mm long. 4 aquatic genera; 8 species. Also many terrestrial species. *Limnophora* occurs in running waters, *Lispe* and *Graphomya* are found in mud and *Phaonia* is a tree hole specialist. *Limnophora* is sometimes included in the family Anthomyiidae.

Dolichopodidae are up to 10 mm long. 22 peripherally aquatic genera; around 100 species. Also many terrestrial species. Wet soil, mud and damp moss, including some in salt marshes and sea shore habitats.

a)   b)

Fig. M42. Muscidae, posterior end of abdomen (dorsal view): (a) *Graphomya*; (c) *Lispe*.

Fig. M43. Scathophagidae.

Key to Diptera pupae

All Diptera go through a complete metamorphosis during the pupal stage and all adult Diptera are terrestrial. Therefore, many families pupate on land. Some families (Stratiomyidae, Syrphidae, Sciomyzidae, Ephydridae, Scathophagidae, Muscidae) pupate in the final larval skin, so they look very similar to the larval form and can be identified using the larval key. Others have a pupal case in which adult structures can be identified, most notably the wings wrapped around the front of the body and legs and antennae held close to the body; a key to these is provided below. Most pupal stages are immobile or with limited capacity to move. The main exceptions to this are the pupae of Chaoboridae, Culicidae and Chironomidae, which are active swimmers, often found hanging vertically in open water.

1   Antenna sheaths present on pupal head (fig. M44). Note: do not confuse
     antenna sheaths with thoracic horns (fig. M1a)—   **2**

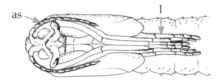

Fig. M44. Tipulidae pupa, ventral view of head and thorax, showing antenna
sheath, *as*, and legs, *l*.

—   No antenna sheaths on pupal head—   **9**

2   Pupa in case fixed to substratum; large multi-filamentous appendages
     on head (fig. M45)—   **Simuliidae**

Fig. M45. Simuliidae pupa, in sheath attached to submerged twig.

—   Pupa free living—   **3**

3   Flattened lobes or paddles present on the end of the abdomen (fig. M1), which may taper to distinct points—   **4**

—   No flattened features on the end of the abdomen—   **6**

4   Swimming paddles present, clearly wider than abdominal segments, with distinct ribs present (see fig. M1b)—

Chaoboridae and Culicidae (fig. M1)

Culicidae have an abdomen that is a normally held curled under the thorax (as in fig. M1a), whereas the abdomen of Chaoboridae is held straight.

—   Abdominal lobes present, very variable in appearance but normally narrower or no wider than abdominal segments and lacking ribs—   **5**

5   Lobes at least twice as long as wide, distinctly tapering to a fine point and without setae or spines—   **Dixidae**

—   Lobes very variable but not longer than wide or, if so, rounded or square ended; setae or spines usually present—   **Chironomidae**

There are a few chironomid pupae with long, pointed lobes, but these will have small setae on them. To make doubly sure, check the thoracic horn (see fig. M1a for how to find this). Dixidae have a thoracic horn that is flared and like an ice cream cone or trumpet in shape (and is also known as a respiratory trumpet); different Chironomidae have a whole variety of shapes, including a feathery tuft, for this feature, but it is never trumpet-shaped.

6(3) Legs extend considerably beyond the end of the wing buds (figs M44, M46)—   **7**

—   Legs shorter or only slightly longer than the wing buds (fig. M47)—   **8**

7   Two appendages on head of clearly different lengths and structure—
Ptychopteridae (fig. M46)

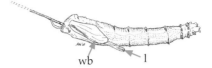

Fig. M46. Ptychopteridae pupa, lateral view, showing legs, *l* and wing buds, *wb*, arrowed.

—   No such appendages on head (fig. M44)—
Tipulidae, Cylindrotomidae, Limoniidae, Pediciidae

8(6) Legs of different lengths, so there is a gradation of pairs between the wing buds—
Psychodidae (fig. M47)

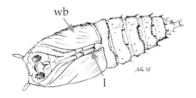

Fig. M47. Psychodidae pupa. Ventral view, with wing buds, *wb* and legs, *l*, arrowed.

—   Legs all apparently of the same length—
Ceratopogonidae and Thaumaleidae

9(1) Long filaments present on the body—   **10**

—   No long filaments—   **11**

10   Filaments on thorax only— **Dolichopodidae**

—   Filaments on thorax and abdomen—
Empididae: Hemerodromiinae (fig. M48)

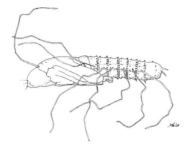

Fig. M48. Hemerodromiinae pupa.

11(9)A pair of curved hooks present at the end of the abdomen—
Empididae: Clinocerinae

—   No abdominal hooks— **12**

12   Abdominal segments with a distinct ring of small bristles—
Tabanidae (fig. M49)

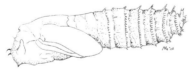

Fig. M49. Tabanidae pupa.

—   Abdominal segments with large, widely dispersed spines—
Rhagionidae and Athericidae

Taking identification further

Improving your knowledge

Our aim at the FBA is to encourage people's interest, knowledge and involvement in freshwater biology. Our reasons are simple: water is vital for human beings and our modern way of life makes increasing demands on a resource which is both limited and under increasing pressure. We believe that few people would wish to damage the environment once they understand the results of their actions. Therefore, to help protect and conserve freshwater organisms, we spread the message about their vulnerability as well as how interesting, beautiful and important to the ecology of fresh waters they are. The more people that care about the life of rivers and lakes the less damage will be done.

We assume that you had an interest in the animals found in fresh waters before you delved into this book but, now you have used it, your enthusiasm is probably heightened and your knowledge of the organisms' identity increased, along with your confidence in your own identification skills. Now you can take things further.

There are many ways in which you can extend the knowledge gained here. The most obvious is to use more advanced guides, and a list of those currently available is provided in the bibliography; look at the FBA website, too, for any new guides that may become available, along with pointers for understanding where older published guides may be misleading (for example by using names that have now changed). There are also some online resources that include tips for identification, and some of these are listed on the website.

Other ways involve gaining practical experience with the assistance of experts. Tentative identifications can be verified by the many enthusiasts, amateur and professional, around. People who know about freshwater animals can be found in many universities, museums, non-governmental organisations (such as the FBA, the county Wildlife Trusts and the Rivers Trusts) and recording groups around the country.

One of the best ways to ensure you keep in touch with what is happening in freshwater biology is by joining the FBA. We help our members with many queries or put them contact with further help if needed. We publish keys and guides to specific groups, which are listed in the bibliography below. We offer a wide range of short courses which can provide opportunities for you to explore groups of animals which are less familiar to you or where you need your memory refreshed; these cover both introductory and advanced levels, with some designed for professional biologists. Most of these courses also cover practical techniques, including methods for collecting in the field.

Another provider of introductory courses is the Field Studies Council, while the Institute of Ecology and Environmental Management (IEEM) provides training in specific methods for particular species of conservation interest, such as crayfish.

In all of these ways, you can enhance your knowledge and increase your enjoyment of a rewarding hobby and at the same time help to protect that part of the natural environment which, being out of sight, is often forgotten – below the water.

Involvement in recording

An interest in identification of freshwater invertebrates can be satisfying in its own right, but there are ways in which you can put your skills to practical use, by becoming part of the community of biological recorders. Records of organisms are immensely important, not only so that we know the distribution of species but also so that we can monitor changes in distribution, the arrival and spread of invasive species, and the efficacy of conservation efforts and habitat management.

Have a look at the National Biodiversity Network (NBN) Gateway (data.nbn.org.uk), an online portal to biological records from throughout the UK, or the Irish National Biodiversity Data Centre Mapping System (maps.biodiversityireland.ie), its equivalent in Ireland (including Northern Ireland). These will allow you to see the distribution of organisms, but also the extent to which they have been recorded and the gaps that still occur in our knowledge of the distribution of so many species.

Many groups of freshwater invertebrates have national recorders, who collate and check records for their own group of interest, and these people are always happy to receive new records. There are also county recording schemes across the country. If one group of animals has captured your interest more than others, there may be a specialist recording organisation with which you can become involved. Relevant contact details for all of these can be found on our website.

Bibliography

The following identification guides are recommended for more detailed identification of freshwater invertebrates. Note that comprehensive guides are not available for many of the smaller groups or, within the insects, for beetle larvae or for many Diptera families. Remember also that name changes and invasive species will have an effect on the value of a guide. Unfortunately, the time and skill required to produce an identification guide means that quite a few of the guides listed are now quite old; for updates, please check the FBA website.

Smaller groups
Class Arachnida
Gerecke, R. (1994). Freshwater mites (Hydrachnellae). An identification key for the genera of Hydrachnellae known from the Palearctic region, with an introductory survey on the water dwelling mites. *Lauterbornia*, **18**, 1-84.

Phylum Bryozoa
Wood, T.S. & Okamura, B. (2005). *A New Key to the Freshwater Bryozoans of Britain, Ireland and Continental Europe, with Notes on their Ecology*. Scientific Publication No. 63. Freshwater Biological Association, Ambleside. 113pp.

Phylum Porifera
Eggers T.O. & Eiseler B. (2007). A key to the freshwater Spongillidae (Porifera) of central and northern Europe. *Lauterbornia*, **60**, 1-53. Text in German; key in German and English.

Phylum Rotifera
Pontin R. (1978). *A Key to the Freshwater Planktonic and Semi-Planktonic Rotifera of the British Isles*. Scientific Publication No. 38. Freshwater Biological Association, Ambleside. 178pp.

Phylum Tardigrada
Morgan, C.I. & King, P.E. (1976). *British Tardigrades. Keys and Notes for the Identification of Species*. Linnean Society Synopses of the British Fauna. New Series No. 9. Academic Press, London. 132pp.

Phylum Turbellaria: flatworms
Reynoldson, T.B. & Young, J.O. (2000). *A Key to the Freshwater Triclads of Britain and Ireland, with Notes on their Ecology*. Scientific Publication No. 58. Freshwater Biological Association, Ambleside. 72pp.

Young J.O. (2001). *Keys to the Freshwater Microturbellarians of Britain and Ireland, with Notes on their Ecology*. Scientific Publication No. 59. Freshwater Biological Association, Ambleside. 142pp.

Phylum Annelida: leeches and true worms
Brinkhurst, R.O. (1971). *A Guide for the Identification of British Aquatic Oligochaeta*. Scientific Publication No. 22. Freshwater Biological Association, Ambleside. [Can be accessed online: see FBA website for details]
Elliott, J.M. & Mann, K.H. (1979). *A Key to the British Freshwater Leeches, with Notes on their Life Cycles and Ecology*. Scientific Publication No. 40. Freshwater Biological Association, Ambleside. 72pp.
Timm, T. (2009). A guide to the freshwater Oligochaeta and Polychaeta of northern and central Europe. *Lauterbornia*, **66**, 1-235.

Phylum Mollusca: snails, limpets and mussels
a. Gastropoda
Macan, T.T. (1977). *A Key to the British Fresh- and Brackish-Water Gastropods, with Notes on their Ecology*. Fourth Edition. Freshwater Biological Association, Scientific Publication No. 13. Freshwater Biological Association, Ambleside. 46pp.
b. Bivalvia
Ellis A.E. (1978). *British Freshwater Bivalve Mollusca*. Linnean Society Synopses of the British Fauna. New Series No. 11. Academic Press, London. 113pp.
Killeen, I., Aldridge, D. & Oliver, G. (2004). *Freshwater Bivalves of Britain and Ireland*. OP82. Field Studies Council, Shrewsbury. 119pp.

Class Crustacea: shrimps, crayfish, water fleas, copepods, ostracods and allies

a. subclass Branchiopoda

Scourfield D.J & Harding J.P. (1966). *A Key to the British Species of Freshwater Cladocera, with Notes on their Ecology*. Third Edition. Scientific Publication No. 5. Freshwater Biological Association, Ambleside. 61pp.

b. subclass Copepoda

Fryer G. (1982). *The Parasitic Copepoda and Branchiura of British Freshwater Fishes: a Handbook and Key*. Scientific Publication No. 46. Freshwater Biological Association, Ambleside. 87pp.

Gurney, R. (1933). *British Fresh-Water Copepoda*. Ray Society, London.

Harding, J.P. & Smith, W.A. (1974). *A Key to the British Freshwater Cyclopoid and Calanoid Copepods, with Ecological Notes*. Second Edition. Scientific Publication No. 18. Freshwater Biological Association, Ambleside. 56pp.

c. subclass Malacostraca

Gledhill, T., Sutcliffe, D.W. & Williams, W.D. (1993). *British Freshwater Crustacea Malacostraca: a Key with Ecological Notes.* Scientific Publication No. 52. Freshwater Biological Association, Ambleside. 176pp.

Dobson, M. (2012). I*dentifying Invasive Freshwater Shrimps and Isopods*. Freshwater Biological Association (free download: see FBA website for details)

Insects

a. smaller orders

Elliott, J.M. (2009). *Freshwater Megaloptera and Neuroptera of Britain and Ireland: Keys to Adults and Larvae, and a Review of their Ecology*. Scientific Publication No. 65. Freshwater Biological Association, Ambleside. 71pp.

Hopkin S.P. (2007) *A Key to the Collembola (Springtails) of Britain and Ireland*. OP111. Field Studies Council, Shrewsbury. 245pp.

b. Ephemeroptera: mayflies

Elliott, J.M. & Humpesch, U.H. (2010). *Mayfly Larvae (Ephemeroptera) of Britain and Ireland: Keys and a Review of their Ecology*. Scientific Publication No. 66. Freshwater Biological Association, Ambleside. 152pp.

c. Plecoptera: stoneflies

Hynes, H.B.N. (1977). *A Key to the Adults and Nymphs of the British Stoneflies (Plecoptera), with Notes on their Ecology and Distribution*. Third Edition. Scientific Publication No. 17. Freshwater Biological Association, Ambleside. 92pp.

d. Odonata: dragonflies and damselflies

Cham, S. (2007). *Field guide to the Larvae and Exuviae of British Dragonflies, Volume 1: Dragonflies (Anisoptera)*. The British Dragonfly Society, Peterborough. 80pp.

Cham, S. (2009). *Field guide to the Larvae and Exuviae of British Dragonflies, Volume 2: Damselflies (Zygoptera)*. The British Dragonfly Society, Peterborough. 76pp.

Hammond, C.O. (1983). *The Dragonflies of Great Britain and Ireland*. Second Edition. Harley Books, Colchester. 116pp.

e. Hemiptera: true bugs

Savage, A.A. (1989). *Adults of the British Hemiptera Heteroptera: a Key with Ecological Notes*. Scientific Publication No. 50. Freshwater Biological Association, Ambleside. 173pp.

Savage, A.A. (1999). *Keys to the Larvae of British Corixidae*. Scientific Publication No. 57. Freshwater Biological Association, Ambleside. 173pp.

f. Trichoptera: caddisflies

Edington, J.M. & Hildrew, A.G. (2005). *A Revised Key to the Caseless Caddis Larvae of the British Isles, with Notes on their Ecology*. Scientific Publication No. 53. Freshwater Biological Association, Ambleside. 134pp.

Wallace, I.D., Wallace, B. & Philipson, G.N. (2003). *Keys to the Case-Bearing Caddis Larvae of Britain and Ireland*. Scientific Publication No. 61. Freshwater Biological Association, Ambleside. 259pp.

Wallace, I.D. (2006). *Simple Key to Caddis Larvae*. OP105, Field Studies Council, Shrewsbury. 64pp.

g. Coleoptera

Friday, L.E. (1988). *A Key to the Adults of British Water Beetles*. Field Studies 7, 1-151. [Can be accessed online: see website for details]

Foster G.N. & Friday L.E. (2011). *Key to Adults of the Water Beetles of Britain and Ireland (Part 1) Second Edition*. Royal Entomological Society Handbook Vol.4, Part 5. Shrewsbury, Field Studies Council. [Covers Gyrinidae, Haliplidae, Noteridae, Paelobiidae and Dytiscidae] 144pp.

Holland D.G. (1972). *A Key to the Larvae, Pupae and Adults of the British species of Elminthidae*. Scientific Publication No. 26. Freshwater Biological Association, Ambleside. [Covers Elmidae] 58pp.

h. Diptera

Bass, J. (1998). *Last-Instar Larvae and Pupae of the Simuliidae of Britain and Ireland: a Key with brief Ecological Notes.* Scientific Publication No. 55. Freshwater Biological Association, Ambleside. 104pp.

Cranston, P.S. (1982). *A Key to the Larvae of the British Orthocladiinae (Chironomidae).* Scientific Publication No. 45. Freshwater Biological Association, Ambleside. 152pp.

Cranston, P.S., Ramsdale, C.D., Snow, K.R. & White, G.B. (1987). *Keys to the Adults, Male Hypopygia, Fourth-Instar Larvae and Pupae of the British Mosquitoes (Culicidae), with Notes on their Ecology and Medical Importance.* Scientific Publication No. 48. Freshwater Biological Association, Ambleside. 152pp.

Disney, R.H.L. (1999). *British Dixidae (Meniscus Midges) and Thaumaleidae (Trickle Midges): Keys with Ecological Notes.* Scientific Publication No. 56. Freshwater Biological Association, Ambleside. 128pp.

Rotheray, G.E. (1993). *Colour Guide to Hoverfly Larvae (Diptera, Syrphidae).* Dipterists Digest No. 9. Derek Whitely, Sheffield. 156pp.

Stubbs, A. & Drake, M. (2001). *British Soldier Flies and their Allies.* British Entomological & Natural History Society, Reading. [Covers Athericidae, Rhagionidae, Tabanidae and Stratiomyidae] 512pp.

Wilson R.S. & Ruse L.P. (2005). *A Guide to the Identification of Genera of Chironomid Pupal Exuviae Occurring in Britain and Ireland (Including Common Genera from Northern Europe) and their Use in Monitoring Lotic and Lentic Fresh Waters.* Special Publication No. 13. Freshwater Biological Association, Ambleside. 176pp.

List and classification of animals covered by this book

The list below shows the classification of the animals covered by this guide. For each, the phylum is given; our keys stop at phylum for some groups, but for the remainder the class, order and family is also given. Subclasses, suborders, subfamilies or tribes are also listed, where these have been used in the keys. Note that the higher classification of many groups is still unclear, so definitive divisions are not always possible. Genera are listed for some groups, where these are used as end points in the key.

At the end of each entry, a number in brackets gives an indication of the number of aquatic species. Sometimes the number of species is clearly known, but new species are being discovered or introduced at frequent intervals, while changes in ideas of relationships sometimes require a species to be removed, so many of these numbers will change over time. Note also that, particularly among the Diptera (true flies), some families are both aquatic and terrestrial and the true number of species with aquatic larvae is simply not known, so the numbers listed may include terrestrial species as well.

Phylum Porifera (sponges)
  Class Demospongiae
      Order Haplosclerida
         Family Spongillidae   4 genera (5)
Phylum Bryozoa (bryozoans)   6 families; 7 genera (11)
Phylum Cnidaria
  Class Hydrozoa
      Order Anthoathecatae **(hydras)**
         Family Hydridae   *Hydra* (4)
         Family Protohydridae   *Protohydra* (1)
         Family Oceanidae   *Cordylophora* (1)
      Order Limnomedusae **(jellyfish)**
         Family Olindiidae   *Craspedacusta* (1)
Phylum Rotifera (rotifers)   27 families; 94 genera (c. 500)
Phylum Gastrotricha   4 families; 11 genera (c. 50)

Phylum Tardigrada   3 families; 4 genera (42)
Phylum Platyhelminthes
  Class Turbellaria
    Order Tricladida **(flatworms)**
        Family Planariidae   *Polycelis* (3), *Phagocata* (2)
                                      Crenobia (1), *Planaria* (1)
        Family Dendrocoelidae   *Dendrocoelium* (1), *Bdellocephala* (1)
        Family Dugesiidae   *Dugesia* (3)
    'Microturbellaria'   11 families; 26 genera (47)
Phylum Nematoda   18 families; 31 genera (70)
Phylum Nematomorpha   2 families; 3 genera (4)
Phylum Nemertea
  Class Enopla
    Order Hoplonemertea
        Family Tetrastemmatidae   *Prostoma* (2)
Phylum Annelida
  Class Clitellaria
    Subclass Hirudinea **(leeches)**
      Order Rhynchobdellida
        Family Glossiphoniidae   6 genera (8)
        Family Piscicolidae   *Piscicola* (1)
      Order Arhynchobdellida
        Family Hirudinidae   2 genera (2)
        Family Erpobdellidae   3 genera (5)
    Subclass Oligochaeta **(true worms)**
      Order Branchiobdellida
        Family Branchiobdellidae   *Branchiobdella* (1)
      Order Haplotaxida
        Family Haplotaxidae   *Haplotaxis* (1)
        Family Enchytraeidae   9 genera (25)
        Family Lumbricidae   7 genera (9)
        Family Sparganophilidae   *Sparganophilus* (1)
        Family Propappidae   *Propappus* (1)
        Family Naididae   14 genera (33)
        Family Tubificidae   17 genera (36)
      Order Lumbriculida
        Family Lumbriculidae   6 genera (10)
  Class Polychaeta (Division into orders not clear)
        Family Aeolosomatidae   *Aeolosoma* (6)

Phylum Mollusca
Class Gastropoda (snails) (Division into orders not clear)
      Family Neritidae   *Theodoxus* (1)
      Family Viviparidae   *Viviparus* (2)
      Family Hydrobiidae   7 genera (7)
      Family Valvatidae   *Valvata* (3)
      Family Bithyniidae   *Bithynia* (2)
      Family Acroloxidae   *Acroloxus* (1)
      Family Lymnaeidae   6 genera (9)
      Family Planorbidae   *Ancylus* (1), *Ferrisia* (1)
              Others: 8 genera (15)
      Family Physidae   3 genera (4)
Class Bivalvia (mussels)
    Order Veneroida
      Family Dreissenidae   2 genera (2)
      Family Sphaeriidae   3 genera (22)
      Family Corbiculidae   *Corbicula* (1)
    Order Unionida
     Superfamily Unionoidea
      Family Margaritiferidae   *Margaritifera* (1)
      Family Unionidae   3 genera (6)
Phylum Arthropoda
Class Arachnida
    Order Araneae **(spiders)**
      Family Cybaeidae   *Argyroneta* (1)
      Family Pisauridae   *Dolomedes* (1)
      Family Lycosidae   *Pirata* (1)
    Order Acari **(mites)**   30 families; 73 genera (c. 300)
Class Crustacea
   Subclass Ostracoda   8 families; 26 genera (c. 90)
   Subclass Branchiopoda
    Order Anostraca **(fairy shrimps)**
      Family Chirocephalidae   *Chirocephalus* (1)
      Family Tanymastigiidae   *Tanymastix* (1)
    Order Notostraca
      Family Triopsidae   *Triops* (1)

Order Ctenopoda	
Family Holopedidae	*Holopedium* (1)
Family Sididae	3 genera (4)
Order Anomapoda	
Family Chydoridae	19 genera (42)
Family Macrothricidae	8 genera (11)
Family Moinidae	*Moina* (3)
Family Daphniidae	3 genera (22)
Family Bosminidae	*Bosmina* (3)
Order Haplopoda	
Family Leptodoridae	*Leptodora* (1)
Order Onychopoda	
Family Polyphemidae	*Polyphemus* (1)
Family Cercopagidae	*Bythotrephes* (2)
Subclass Branchiura	
Order Arguloida	
Family Argulidae	*Argulus* (3)
Subclass Copepoda	
Order Harpacticoida	8 families; 16 genera (43)
Order Calanoida	4 families; 8 genera (16)
Order Cyclopoida	4 families; 20 genera (47)
Order Poecilistomatoida	1 family; 3 genera (5)
Order Siphonostomatoida	2 families; 4 genera (7)
Subclass Malacostraca	
Order Bathynellacea	
Family Bathynellidae	*Antrobathynella* (1)
Order Isopoda	
Family Asellidae	*Proasellus* (2), *Asellus* (1), *Caecidotea* (1)
Family Sphaeromatidae	*Lekanesphaera* (2)
Family Janiridae	*Jaera* (1)
Order Amphipoda **(shrimps)**	
Family Corophiidae	2 genera (5)
Family Talitridae	*Orchestia* (1)
Family Niphargidae	*Niphargus* (5)
Family Crangonyctidae	*Crangonyx* (2)
Family Gammaridae	*Gammarus* (5), *Dikerogammarus* (2), *Echinogammarus* (1)

Order Decapoda **(crabs and crayfish)**
    Family Grapsidae   *Eriocheir* (1)
    Family Cambaridae   2 genera (2)
    Family Astacidae   *Austropotamobius* (1), *Astacus* (2)
                                    Pacifastacus (1)
    Family Palaemonidae   2 genera (2)
Order Mysidacea
    Family Mysidae   *Mysis* (1), *Neomysis* (1),
                                      Hemimysis (1)

Class Entognatha
 Subclass Collembola   6 families; 13 genera (22)
Class Insecta
    Order Megaloptera
        Family Sialidae   *Sialis* (3)
    Order Lepidopotera
        Family Crambidae   5 genera (5)
    Order Neuroptera
        Family Sisyridae   *Sisyra* (1)
        Family Osmylidae   *Osmylus* (1)
    Order Hymenoptera   11 families (c.40)
    Order Ephemeroptera **(mayflies)**
        Family Caenidae   2 genera (9)
        Family Ephemeridae   *Ephemera* (3)
        Family Potamanthidae   *Potamanthus* (1)
        Family Arthropleidae   *Arthroplea* (1)
        Family Heptageniidae   *Ecdyonurus* (3), *Rhithrogena* (2)
                                    Heptagenia (3), *Electrogena* (2)
        Family Ephemerellidae   *Serratella* (1), *Ephemerella* (1)
        Family Leptophlebiidae   *Habrophlebia* (1), *Leptophlebia* (2)
                                    Paraleptophlebia (3)
        Family Baetidae   *Baetis* (9), *Procloeon* (2)
                                    Centroptilum (1), *Cloeon* (2)
        Family Ameletidae   *Ameletus* (1)
        Family Siphlonuridae   *Siphlonurus* (3)

Order Plecoptera **(stoneflies)**
    Family Taeniopterygidae   *Taeniopteryx*(1), *Rhabdiopteryx*(1), *Brachyptera* (2)
    Family Nemouridae   *Protonemura* (3), *Amphinemura* (2) *Nemurella* (1), *Nemoura* (6)
    Family Capniidae   *Capnia* (3)
    Family Leuctridae   *Leuctra* (6)
    Family Perlidae   *Dinocras* (1), *Perla* (1)
    Family Chloroperlidae   3 genera (3)
    Family Perlodidae   *Perlodes* (1), *Diura* (1), *Isogenus* (1)
Order Odonata
  Suborder Zygoptera **(damselflies)**
    Family Calopterygidae   *Calopteryx* (2)
    Family Lestidae   2 genera (5)
    Family Coenagrionidae   6 genera (12)
    Family Platycnemididae   *Platycnemis* (1)
  Suborder Anisoptera **(dragonflies)**
    Family Aeshnidae   4 genera (12)
    Family Gomphidae   *Gomphus* (2)
    Family Cordulegastridae   *Cordulegaster* (1)
    Family Corduliidae   2 genera (3)
    Family Libellulidae   6 genera (17)
Order Hemiptera **(bugs)**
    Family Hydrometridae   *Hydrometra* (2)
    Family Mesoveliidae   *Mesovelia* (1)
    Family Hebridae   *Hebrus* (2)
    Family Veliidae   2 genera (5)
    Family Gerridae   3 genera (10)
    Family Corixidae   9 genera (37)
    Family Nepidae   *Nepa* (1), *Ranatra* (1)
    Family Naucoridae   2 genera (2)
    Family Aphelocheiridae   *Aphelocheirus* (1)
    Family Pleidae   *Plea* (1)
    Family Notonectidae   *Notonecta* (4)

Order Trichoptera **(caddisflies)**

Family Hydropsychidae	*Cheumatopsyche* (1)
	Hydropsyche (9), *Diplectrona* (1)
Family Ecnomidae	*Ecnomus* (1)
Family Hydroptilidae	7 genera (31)
Family Glossosomatidae	
Subf. Agapetinae	*Agapetus* (3), *Synagapetus* (1)
Subf. Glossosomatinae	*Glossosoma* (3)
Family Rhyacophilidae	*Rhyacophila* (4)
Family Phyganeidae	6 genera (10)
Family Philopotamidae	*Wormaldia* (3), *Chimarra* (1)
	Philopotamus (1)
Family Psychomyiidae	4 genera (12)
Family Polycentropodidae	5 genera (13)
Family Goeridae	*Goera* (1), *Silo* (2)
Family Lepidostomatidae	3 genera (5)
Family Limnephilidae	20 genera (55)
Family Apataniidae	*Apatania* (4)
Family Molannidae	*Molanna* (2)
Family Brachycentridae	*Brachycentrus* (1)
Family Beraeidae	4 genera (5)
Family Leptoceridae	10 genera (31)
Family Sericostomatidae	*Sericostoma* (1), *Notidobia* (1)
Family Odontoceridae	*Odontocerum* (1)

Order Coleoptera **(beetles)**

Family Curculionidae	24 genera (57)
Family Chrysomelidae	4 genera (22)
Family Elmidae	8 genera (12)
Family Haliplidae	3 genera (19)
Family Hygrobiidae	*Hygrobia* (1)
Family Noteridae	*Noterus* (2)
Family Dytiscidae	29 genera (119)
Family Gyrinidae	2 genera (12)
Family Dryopidae	2 genera (9)
Family Hydrophilidae	17 genera (70)
Family Hydrochidae	*Hydrochus* (7)
Family Hydraenidae	4 genera (32)
Family Helophoridae	*Helophorus* (20)
Family Spercheidae	*Spercheus* (1)

Family Sphaeriuscidae	*Sphaerius* (1)
Family Georissidae	*Georissus* (1)
Family Scirtidae	7 genera (20)
Family Psephenidae	*Eubria* (1)
Family Limnichidae	*Limnichius* (1)
Family Heteroceridae	2 genera (8)
Order Diptera (true flies)	
Family Ceratopogonidae	
Subf. Forcipomyinae	*Atrichopogon* (13), *Forcipomyia*(26)
Subf. Dayheleinae	*Dasyhelea* (11)
Subf. Ceratopogoninae	17 genera (111)
Family Simuliidae	3 genera (33)
Family Dixidae	*Dixa* (6), *Dixella* (9)
Family Thaumaleidae	*Thaumalea* (3)
Family Chironomidae	
Subf. Tanypodinae	26 genera (63)
Subf. Podonominae	3 genera (3)
Subf. Chironominae	
Tribe Tanytarsini	12 genera (102)
Tribe Chironomini	34 genera (c.145)
Subf. Prodiamesinae	3 genera (5)
Subf. Orthocladiinae	51 genera (c.250)
Subf. Diamesinae	7 genera (17)
Family Chaoboridae	*Chaoborus* (4), *Mochlonyx* (2)
Family Culicidae	
Subf. Culicinae	*Culex* (4), *Culiseta* (7), *Aedes* (3), *Dahliana* (1), *Ochlerotatus* (11), *Coquillettidia* (1), *Orthopodomyia* (1)
Subf. Anophelinae	*Anopheles* (6)
Family Ptychopteridae	*Ptychoptera* (7)
Family Psychodidae	
Subf. Sycoracinae	*Sycorax* (3)
Subf. Psychodinae	
Tribe Psychodini	2 genera (16)
Tribe Pericomini	6 genera (32)
Tribe Telmatoscopini	7 genera (41)
Family Cylindrotomidae	*Triogma* (1), *Phalacrocera* (1)
Family Tipulidae	5 genera (45)
Family Pediciidae	3 genera (17)

Family Limoniidae	50 genera (c.200)
Family Athericidae	*Atrichops* (1), *Atherix* (1), *Ibisia* (1)
Family Rhagionidae	*Chrysophilus* (2), *Rhagio* (10)
Family Tabanidae	
Subf. Chrysopsinae	*Chrysops* (4)
Subf. Tabaninae	
Tribe Haematopotini	*Haematopota* (5)
Tribe Tabanini	3 genera (21)
Family Stratiomyidae	
Subf. Beridinae	*Beris* (6)
Subf. Clitellarinae	*Nemotelus* (4), *Oxycera* (11), *Vanoya* (1)
Subf. Stratiomyinae	*Stratiomys* (4), *Odontomyia* (6), *Oplodontha* (1)
Family Empididae	
Subf. Clinocerinae	4 genera (17)
Subf. Hemerodrominae	5 genera (24)
Other subfamilies	3 genera (25)
Family Dolichopodidae	22 genera (c. 100)
Family Syrphidae	
Tribe Eristalini	8 genera (28)
Tribe Sericomyiini	2 genera (3)
Tribe Chrysogasterini	*Melanogaster* (2), *Neoascia* (6) Others: 5 genera (11)
Tribe Spheginini	*Sphegina* (4)
Family Sciomyzidae	16 genera (c.50)
Family Ephydridae	*Ephydra* (2), *Setacera* (3) *Notophila* (15), *Hydrellia* (10) Others: 6 genera (10)
Family Scathophagidae	9 genera (9)
Family Muscidae	*Limnophora* (1), *Lispe* (8), *Graphomya* (2), *Phaonia* (2)

Acknowledgements

We wish to thank the following people for their contributions during the production of this guide.

For the supply, loan or access to specimens, we thank: Rosie Blackman and Richard Chadd (Environment Agency), Dmitri Logunov (Manchester Museum), James Pretty (Queen Mary University of London), David Pryce (Plecoptera Recording Scheme), Graham Rotheray (National Museums of Scotland) and Ian Wallace (World Museum Liverpool).

For inputs to development of the keys and comments on earlier versions, we thank: John Blackburn, Richard Chadd, John Davy-Bowker, Haifa Jaweir, James Pretty and Ian Wallace. We particularly thank Geoffrey Fryer and Jim Green for reviewing and improving early versions of all the keys.

This book was produced thanks to a grant from the Esmée Fairbairn Foundation.

Figure acknowledgements

We are grateful to the following for permission to use their figures.

Tom Macan, for allowing us to use the following from his father's book: A2, 3a, 8; D2, 3, 4, 5, 6; E5, 11a, 20; I2a.

Ray Society, for E11d, originally published in Gurney, R. (1933). *British Freshwater Copepoda. III. Cyclopoida*. Ray Society, London. 384pp.

John Wiley & Sons Ltd, for B7, originally published in *Journal of Zoology* vol 193, page 533 (1981).

L.S. Bellamy, for B8.

Graham Bird, for allowing us to use the following from an unpublished manuscript: C3, 4, 5, 6, 7, 8, 9.

Geoffrey Fryer, for E1, 2, 3, 4.

Terry Gledhill, for N2.

The following figures were taken from earlier FBA publications, those for which FBA holds copyright, or from publications that we now understand are out of copyright:

A3b is by J. Green, originally published in *Freshwater Forum* **11** (1) (1998)

A4 left, 5, 6, 9, 10; E1, 2, 3, 4, 7, 8b,c,d,f,g, 9, 10, 11b,c; F3, 6d are from Fryer, G. (1991) *A Natural History of the Lakes, Tarns and Streams of the English Lake District*.

A4 middle and right are by R. Pontin, from Pontin (1978) *A Key to the Freshwater Planktonic and Semi-Planktonic Rotifera of the British Isles*.

B1-6 are from Reynoldson & Young (2000). *A Key to the Freshwater Triclads of Britain and Ireland, with Notes on their Ecology*.

C2a,b are from Elliott & Mann (1979). *A Key to the British Freshwater Leeches, with Notes on their Life Cycles and Ecology.*

E6 is by J.C. Schaeffer 1756.

E8a, e are from Scourfield & Harding (1966) *A Key to the British Species of Freshwater Cladocera, with Notes on their Ecology. Third Edition.*

E13b-e, 16, 18c,d, 19a,b are from Gledhill et al. (1993) *British Freshwater Crustacea Malacostraca: a Key with Ecological Notes,* E12 and 14 were drawn by Terry Gledhill based on originals by A. Thienemann and G. Sars, respectively.

F5a, 8 are from Elliott, J.M. (2009). *Freshwater Megaloptera and Neuroptera of Britain and Ireland: Keys to Adults and Larvae, and a Review of their Ecology.*

J1, 2a, 3, ,4a, 5a, 6, 9, 10, 11, 12a,b are by T.T. Macan, and F5b; J2b, 4b, 5b, 7, 8 are by T.T. Macan, modified by A.A. Savage, from Savage (1989) *Adults of the British Aquatic Hemiptera Heteroptera: a Key with Ecological Notes.*

K1, 4, 5, 7a,c,d, 8a,c,d, 9a, 10a,c,d, 11, 12c, 15b-d, 17, 18, 19a,c, 20, 21c, 22d, 23b-d, 24c, 25c, 26c-f, 27a,c plus the adult caddisfly in the introduction are from Hickin (1967) *Caddis Larvae.* Hutchinson of London. All are by N.E. Hickin, other than K4a, by G.N Philipson, and K5b, by A. Neilsen.

The artists responsible for many early figures used by the FBA were not recorded and, if we have made any mistakes in our assumption of copyright, we will gladly correct these in future editions.

All other figures and illustrations are originals.

The water colour images are by Dr Peter Ayres.

The following are by Simon Pawley: C2c; E23b,c,d; G2b; I2b, 3, 4, 5, 6, 8, 9; L2, 3, 4, 5, 6, 7, 8, 9, 11.

All remaining figures in the text are by Michael Dobson.

Front cover photos are by Roy Anderson (*Bithynia leachii*), Simon Booth (*Dytiscus marginalis*) and from Oceans-Image/Photoshot (*Ecdyonurus* sp.).

Glossary

A word highlighted in **bold** in the definition will have its own definition elsewhere in the glossary.

Abdomen – the **posterior** part of the body of an **arthropod** (see fig. N1).

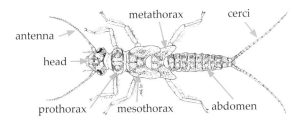

Fig. N1. The general body parts of an insect larva.

Abdominal: referring to the **abdomen**.

Antenna (plural: **antennae**) – sensory organs found in most arthropods that occur in pairs attached to the **anterior** body **segment** in the head. Antennae are normally subdivided into a series of smaller units, often referred to as **segments**. Crustaceans have two pairs of antennae; insects have one pair and spiders have none.

Anterior – towards the end of an animal where the head or mouth is situated, normally equivalent to the 'front' of most animals. The opposite of anterior is **posterior**.

Aperture – in gastropod snails: the opening into the shell within which the animal can contract its soft body tissues.

Arthropod – an animal in the phylum Arthropoda, the jointed legged invertebrates, including insects, spiders and crustaceans.

Bivalve – comprising two parts, similar in size and shape, that can move relative to each other. Also refers to molluscs of the class Bivalvia (mussels), which have two shells joined by a hinge.

Caecum (plural: **caeca**) – a small pouch in the gut of an animal.

Calcareous or **calcified** – composed of calcium carbonate and therefore hardened and inflexible. Refers particularly to structures in molluscs.

Carapace – a hardened plate covering part of the **dorsal** surface of an animal and hiding the **segments** and appendages beneath.

Carpus – a crustacean leg segment. Among crabs and crayfish, the segment to which the large anterior pincer is attached.

Caudal – referring to the posterior of the abdomen. Caudal process – an elongate extension to the posterior abdominal segment of an arthropod. Includes the breathing tube of many Hemiptera (true bugs) and the middle tail of Ephemeroptera (mayflies).

Cephalothorax – the combined head and thorax of spiders and crustaceans, in which they are not clearly differentiated, unlike in insects. Also referred to as the **prosoma** in spiders and mites.

Cerci (singular: **cercus**) – a pair of appendages on the posterior segment of many **arthropods**. Includes the tails of Plecoptera (stoneflies) and the outer tails of Ephemeroptera (mayflies).

Chaetae (singular: **chaeta**) – see **setae**.

Chitinous – made of chitin, a tough, protective substance that forms the exoskeleton of most arthropods.

Cilia (singular: **cilium**) – a slender, flexible extension. **Ciliate** – possessing cilia.

Classification – the hierarchical ordering of species according to their relationships with each other. All species have six levels of classification in the accepted system used by zoologists:

Kingdom (plural: kingdoms)
Phylum (plural: phyla)
Class (plural: classes)
Order (plural: orders)
Family (plural: families)
Genus (plural: genera)
Species (plural: species)

So two species which share the same genus are very closely related, two species in different genera but the same family are more distantly related, while two species in different phyla are very distantly related.

In addition, where it is considered that differentiation is useful but not enough to justify full division into the categories listed above, then super- or sub- categories can be used. For example, several families may be grouped into a superfamily, two or more superfamilies into a suborder and two or more suborders into an order. In this guide, reference is made to subclasses, suborders, subfamilies, tribes (which are further divisions of subfamilies) and subgenera, plus one subspecies.

Clitellum – a thickened part of the body of oligochaete worms, present when the animal is sexually mature.

Coxa (plural: **coxae**) – see **jointed leg**.

Cuticle – the outer protective layer, usually flexible (**membranous**), of many invertebrates.

Dextral - oriented to the right. Refers to the shell **aperture** of gastropod snails: when held with the aperture towards the observer, if is to the right it is referred to as dextral, in contrast to **sinistral**.

Distal – further from the body. Contrasts with proximal, meaning closer to the body. Used when referring to features such as segments of legs.

Dorsal – on or towards the upper side of an animal. The opposite of **ventral**.

Dorso-lateral – referring to the part of an animal's body on the upper part of the side.

Elytra (singular: **elytron**) – the paired wing cases of a beetle. They are modified forewings, hardened to provide a protective cover for the hindwing.

Endemic – found nowhere else in the world.

Endopterygota – see **Holometabolous**.

Exopterygota – see **Hemimetabolous**.

Exoskeleton – the external supporting skeleton of an invertebrate. Hardened parts and supporting structures are on the outside of the animal, in contrast to the endoskeleton, or internal skeleton, of vertebrates.

Femur (plural: **femora**) – see **jointed leg**.

Frontoclypeus – the front edge of the head capsule of an insect.

Gastropod – a snail of the class Gastropoda, with a single coiled or cone-shaped shell.

Genus (plural: **genera**) – a division in the **classification** of organisms. The genus is the next level above the **species**, and each species is given a binomial name including the genus name. See **species** for an example.

Gill – a respiratory organ of an aquatic animal. Invertebrate gills are usually external and normally plate-like, feathery or otherwise adapted to have a large surface area.

Glossae (singular: **glossa**) – paired appendages in the mouthparts of an insect. See **labium**.

Gnathopod – the forelimbs of crustaceans such as shrimps which are adapted for feeding rather than movement (see fig. E16, page 63).

Head capsule – the hardened outer covering of the head, particularly of insects.

Hemimetabolous – referring to insects that lack a pupal stage in their development, so the larvae (sometimes referred to as **nymphs**) are superficially similar to the adults. Often considered a subclass of the insect class, the Exopterygota. Includes Ephemeroptera (mayflies), Plecoptera (stoneflies), Odonata (dragonflies and damselflies), and Hemiptera (true bugs).

Holometabolous – referring to insects with a full metamorphosis incorporating a **pupal** stage between larva and adult, so that the larvae are very different in form to the adults. Often considered a subclass of the insect class, the Endopterygota. Includes Coleoptera (beetles), Trichoptera (caddis flies), Neuroptera (alderflies), Lepidoptera (moths) and Diptera (true flies).

Interstitial – occurring within the spaces between particles of loose sediment, such as sand or pebbles.

Jointed leg – a type of leg possessed by most **arthropods**, comprising a series of separate segments, with a movable joint between each. Insect legs consist of five components: coxa, trochanter, femur, tibia and tarsus (fig. N2); of these, each is a single segment apart from the tarsus, whose number of segments varies from three to seven. Crustaceans and arachnids have a greater number of leg segments.

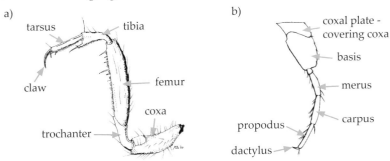

Fig. N2. Segments of the leg of: (a) an insect; (b) a crustacean.

Labium (plural: **labia**) – the lower part of the mouth of insects, variously adapted depending on mode of feeding. In Odonata it is the plate-like **mask**; in Hemiptera, it is the tubular **rostrum**. It comprises several parts. The postmentum, **proximal** to the head, is sometimes divided into the

submentum, normally a broad protective plate, and the **mentum**. The **prementum** is attached to the **distal** margin of the postmentum and contains several appendages used in identifying various insect types: the labial **palps, glossae** and **paraglossae**. See fig. N3.

Labial – referring to the labium.

Labrum – part of the mouth of an insect, at the **anterior** edge, normally in the form of a flattened plate (see fig. N3).

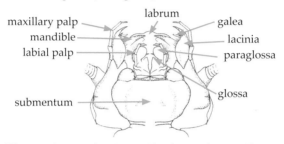

maxillary palp
mandible
labial palp
labrum
galea
lacinia
paraglossa
submentum
glossa

Fig. N3. The mouthparts of an insect. This figure shows a Plecopteran; in other orders, such as Odonata and Hemiptera, some mouthparts can be highly modified.

Lamella (plural: **lamellae**) – a thin, flattened structure.

Larva (plural: **larvae**) – the immature stage of an animal that is morphologically very different from the adult form. **Larval** – referring to the larva. Now often used to refer to all juvenile invertebrates (see **nymph**).

Lateral – on or towards the side of an animal.

Lorica – the protective external case of a rotifer.

Mandible – a paired mouthpart, normally used for biting (see fig. N3).

Mask – in Odonata, the plate-like **labium**, used as a prey catching organ.

Maxilla (plural: **maxillae**) – a paired structure posterior to the **mandibles** of arthropods, part of the mouthparts. **Maxillary** – referring to the maxilla.

Medial – referring to the middle of a feature.

Medusa (plural: **medusae**) – the name given to the round floating stage of jellyfish.

Membranous – referring to the outer surface of the body (or body part) of an animal; made of a soft, flexible membrane, in contrast to **sclerotised**.

Mentum – see **labium**.

Mesonotum – see **thorax**.

Mesodorsum – see **thorax**.

Mesothorax – see **thorax**.

Metadorsum – see **thorax**.

Metanotum – see **thorax**.

Metathorax – see **thorax**.

Nauplius – the first **larval** stage of many crustaceans.

Nymph – a juvenile form of an insect that is **hemimetabolous**, so that the juvenile form is superficially similar to the adult form, often with developing **wing buds**. Formerly used in contrast to the term **larva** – applied to juveniles of insects that are **holometabolous**, so juveniles and adults are very different – but this differentiation is falling out of favour and the term larva is now widely used for both types of juvenile form.

Ocellus (plural: **ocelli**) – a simple eye spot.

Operculum – a hardened flat plate that is used by some gastropod snails to cover the **aperture** of the shell once the animal has withdrawn into it.

Operculate – possessing an operculum.

Opisthosoma – the name given to the abdomen of a spider, to distinguish it from the **Prosoma**.

Palps – paired appendages on the head of some invertebrates, used as sensory organs.

Papilla (plural: papillae) – a small rounded projection.

Paraglossae (singular: **paraglossa**) – paired appendages in the mouthparts of an insect. See **labium**.

Paraprocts – paired **ventral** plates on the most **posterior** abdominal **segment** of insects.

Parasite – an animal that lives attached to or within another animal, gaining nourishment from its host without providing the host animal with anything in return.

Parasitoid – an animal whose larval stage lives within the body of another organism, consuming it from the inside and eventually killing it. Refers particularly to many species of wasps, which prey on other insects in this way.

Pecten – a row of bristles or small spines on the posterior respiratory siphon of some Diptera larvae.

Pereopod – the walking limb of a crustacean (see fig. E16, page 63).

Pharynx – the **anterior** part of the digestive system, immediately behind the mouth.

Phylum (plural: **phyla**) – one of the divisions used in classification. A major division into fundamental types of animals.

Plastron – an air-store, used by air-breathing invertebrates to carry air under water. Fine setae or scales are used to trap a layer of air close to the animal's body.

Pleosome – the **anterior segments** of the **abdomen** of crustaceans such as shrimps, anterior to the **urosome** (see fig. E16, page 63).

Posterior – towards the end of an animal opposite to that where the head or mouth is situated, normally equivalent to the 'back' of most animals. The opposite of posterior is **anterior**.

Prehensile – able to grasp and hold objects.

Prementum – see **labium**.

Proboscis – a trunk-like extension to the head of an animal.

Procercus (plural: **procerci**) – a **posterior** extension to the posterior **abdominal segment** of chironomid larvae (true flies: Diptera).

Prodorsum – see **thorax**.

Proleg – a soft unjointed extension used in locomotion. Among insects, many Diptera (true fly) larvae, which lack **jointed legs**, have prolegs instead. Moth larvae (caterpillars) have both **jointed legs** and prolegs.

Pronotum – see **thorax**.

Prosoma – see **cephalothorax**.

Prosternum – see **thorax**.

Prostomium – in annelids, the part of the head **anterior** to the mouth.

Prothorax – see **thorax**.

Proximal – see **distal**.

Pupa (plural: **pupae**) – a stage in the life cycle of a **holometabolous** insect in which metamorphosis from larva to adult occurs. During the pupal stage, the animal is enclosed in a protective case, does not feed and, with a few exceptions, is immobile. **Pupal** – referring to the pupa.

Ramus – a branch of a crustacean appendage.

Rostrum – an extension to the head of some invertebrates. Important in Hemiptera (true bugs), where it is a **labium** modified into a piercing organ.

Scape – the first segment of an **antenna**.

Sclerotised – hardened and normally darkened. **Sclerite** – a small hardened plate on an otherwise soft **cuticle**.

Scutellum – a small triangular plate between the **elytra** of a Coleoptera (beetle) or the wing bases of some Hemiptera (true bugs).

Segment – a division of the body of an animal. Segments often follow a repeating pattern of similar divisions, which may continue along the length of the animal's body (e.g. segmented worms), or be divisible into larger body sections, called talmata, that consist of segments serving similar functions (e.g. **thorax** and **abdomen** of insects). Segmentation may be hidden by external features such as a **carapace** or **elytra**, but any animal that has **jointed legs**, wings or jointed **antennae** will be segmented, each pair of such appendages deriving from a single segment. The word segment is also used to refer to separate components of arthropod structures that are subdivided, including **jointed legs** and **antennae**.

Setae (singular: **seta**) – A hair-like bristle. The term 'hair' is often used, and although technically incorrect gives a good indication of the structure of a seta. Also referred to as **chaetae**, especially when referring to annelids.

Siphon – an extended tube used for breathing. Particularly associated with families of Diptera (true flies) that obtain oxygen from the air: the siphon is used to pierce the surface film of water while the animal remains otherwise submerged.

Sinistral – oriented to the left. Refers to the shell **aperture** of gastropod snails: when held with the aperture towards the observer, if is to the left it is referred to as sinistral, in contrast to **dextral**.

Species – A group of individuals capable of interbreeding and producing viable offspring; normally also sharing a group of morphological characteristics that are different from those of other animals, and which can be used to identify the species. The natural unit in the **classification** of animals. All known species are given a binomial name, written in italics (or underlined) comprising the **genus** name and the species name, for example *Gammarus pulex*, the species *pulex* in the genus *Gammarus*.

Spicule – a small hook or spine.

Spiracle – a breathing hole connecting the internal respiratory system of insects with the air.

Spiracular disc – a structure at the posterior end of many Diptera (true flies) **larvae**: a circular feature containing two **spiracles** and with lobes on its outer edge.

Sternum – the ventral side of a **segment**. **Sternal** – referring to the sternum.

Submentum – see **labium**.

Tarsus (plural: **tarsi**) – see **jointed leg**. **Tarsal** – referring to the tarsus.

Telson – the last division of the abdomen of a crustacean.

Tentacle – slender movable organ on the head of an invertebrate.

Tergum – the **dorsal** side of a **segment**. **Tergal** – referring to the tergum.

Thorax – the part of the body of an **arthropod** that includes the **segments** immediately behind the head (see fig. N1). The thorax of insects comprises three segments – the prothorax (**anterior**), mesothorax (middle) and metathorax (**posterior**) – to which legs and wings, where present, are attached. The terms prodorsum, mesodorsum and metadorsum, used particularly in identification of caddis larvae, refer to the **dorsal** side of each thoracic segment; their equivalent terms for the **ventral** side are prosternum, etc. The terms pronotum, mesonotum and metanotum, also used in caddis larva identification, refer to the hardened plates on the dorsal side of each segment. In arachnids and crustaceans, the thorax is fused with the head to form the **cephalothorax**. **Thoracic** – referring to the thorax.

Thoracic horn – a paired external respiratory organ found in some Diptera **pupae**, attached to the **dorsal** side of the **thorax**.

Urosome – the **posterior segments** of the **abdomen** of crustaceans such as shrimps, **posterior** to the **pleosome** (see fig. E16, page 63).

Ventral – on or towards the lower side of an animal. The opposite of **dorsal**.

Vestigial – referring to an organ that no longer performs a function for an animal and is therefore normally reduced in size relative to the equivalent organ on an animal for which it still serves a useful purpose.

Wing bud – a developing wing on the **thorax** of **hemimetabolous** insect **larvae**. Wing buds are absent from very young larvae but gradually grow as the larva matures.

Index

Dugesiidae 31, 185
Dytiscidae 141, 146, 182

E

earthworm 38
Ecdyonurus 83, 188
Echinogammarus 49, 65, 187
Echinogammarus berilloni 65
Echinogammarus ischnus 65
Ecnomidae 117, 136, 190
Ecnomus tenellus 117
Electrogena 84, 188
Electrogena affinis 84
Electrogena lateralis 84
Elmidae 140, 145, 182, 190
Elminthidae 140, 182
Eloeophila 164
Empididae 169, 171, 176, 192
Enchytraeidae 36, 38, 185
Entognatha 24, 75, 188
Entoprocta 11, 21
Epeorus 74
Ephemera 81, 188
Ephemerella notata 85
Ephemerellidae 84, 188
Ephemeridae 81, 188
Ephemeroptera 11, 72, 74, 80, 181, 188,
        195, 197, 200
Ephoron virgo 81
Ephydra 169, 192
Ephydridae 169, 170, 173, 192
Ergasilidae 49
Ergasilus 49
Eriocheir sinensis 68
Eristalini 166, 192
Erpobdellidae 35, 185
Eubria palustris 145

F

fairy fly 77
fairy shrimp 52, 186
Ferrissia clessiniana 42, 45

Ferrissia wautieri 45
Finlaya 157
fish leech 35
fish louse 58
flatworm 27, 28, 180, 185
fluke 28
fly, fairy 77
fly, moth 159
fly, true 23, 72, 73, 148, 184, 191, 200, 204
Forcipomyia 151, 191
Forcipomyinae 151, 191

G

Gammaridae 49, 64, 187
Gammarus 49, 65, 187, 205
Gammarus duebeni 65
Gammarus lacustris 65
Gammarus pulex 12, 65, 205
Gammarus tigrinus 65
Gammarus zaddachi 65
Gastropoda 41, 180, 186, 199
gastrotrich 23
Gastrotricha 23, 184
Georissidae 138, 191
Georissus crenulatus 138
Gerridae 108, 189
Glossiphoniidae 35, 185
Glossosomatidae 113, 118, 119, 135, 190
Glossosomatinae 120, 190
Goera 123, 190
Goera pilosa 123
Goeridae 77, 135, 190
golden-ringed dragonfly 103
Gomphidae 103, 189
Gomphus 103, 189
Gordian worm 27
Graphomya 171, 172, 192
Grapsidae 68, 188
greater water boatman 112
Gyrinidae 142, 146, 182, 190

phantom midge 156
Philopotamidae 120, 136, 190
Philopotamus montanus 121
Phryganeidae 113, 119, 135
Physa 45
Physa fontinalis 45
Physella 45
Physella acuta 45
Physidae 45, 186
Pirata piscatorius 25
Pisauridae 25, 186
Piscicola geometra 35
Piscicolidae 35, 185
Placobdella costata 35
Planaria torva 32
Planariidae 29, 30, 31, 32, 185
Planorbidae 42, 45, 186
Platycnemididae 102, 189
Platycnemis pennipes 102
Platyhelminthes 28, 185
Plea leachi 112
Plea minutissima 112
Plecoptera 9, 72, 74, 90, 181, 189, 193,
        197, 200
Pleidae 112, 189
Podonominae 154, 191
Podura aquatica 75
Poecilistomatoida 49, 187
Polycelis 29, 185
Polycelis felina 29
Polycelis nigra 29
Polycelis tenuis 29
Polycentropidae 122
Polycentropodidae 122, 136, 190
Polychaeta 33, 36, 180, 185
Polymitarcidae 11, 81
Polynema natans 77
Polyphemidae 57, 187
Polyphemus pediculus 57
pond skater 108
pond snail 45
Pontogammaridae 64
Porifera 20, 179, 184
Potamanthidae 81, 188

Potamanthus luteus 81
Potamopyrgus antipodarum 10, 44
Potamopyrgus jenkinsi 10, 44
prawn 11, 70
Pristina 39
Pristinidae 39
Proasellus cavaticus 61
Proasellus meridianus 61
Procambarus clarkii 11, 68
Procloeon bifidum 88
Procloeon pennulatum 88
Prodiamesinae 155, 191
Propappidae 185
Propappus volki 39
Prostoma 27, 185
Protist 7
Protohydra leuckarti 22
Protohydridae 22, 184
Protonemura 94, 189
Protozoa 7
Psephenidae 138, 145, 191
Pseudanodonta 46
Psychoda 160
Psychodidae 159, 175, 191
Psychodinae 160, 191
Psychodini 160, 191
Psychomyiidae 122, 136, 190
Ptychoptera 158, 191
Ptychopteridae 158, 175, 191
Pyralidae 78

Q

quagga mussel 45

R

Radix balthica 10, 45
raft spider 25
ramshorn snail 45
Ranatra linearis 110
rat-tailed maggot 166
red swamp crayfish 68
Rhabdiopteryx acuminata 93